AGRICULTURAL COMMISSIONER
COUNTY OF RIVERSIDE
4080 Lemon Street, Room 19
Riverside, California 92501

SUPPLEMENT

to the

Check List of Plant and Soil Nematodes

SUPPLEMENT (1961-1965)
to the
Check List of Plant and Soil Nematodes

A Nomenclatorial Compilation

ARMEN C. TARJAN

When a man's knowledge is not in order, the more of it he has the greater will be his confusion.

—HERBERT SPENCER

University of Florida Press
Gainesville
1967

A UNIVERSITY OF FLORIDA PRESS BOOK

PUBLISHED UNDER THE SPONSORSHIP OF
THE AGRICULTURAL EXPERIMENT STATIONS
OF THE
UNIVERSITY OF FLORIDA

PRINTED BY ROSE PRINTING COMPANY, INC.
TALLAHASSEE, FLORIDA

To the late Drs. Gotthold Steiner and J. Basil Goodey
whose contributions to plant and soil nematology
can never be forgotten

Preface

AN UNDERTAKING such as the construction of this Supplement is rarely the product of a sole person's labors—nor has it been in this case. A number of independent minds were probed to evaluate the practicality and desirability of the style of presentation employed. Drs. A. Coomans of Gent, Belgium; A. M. Golden of Beltsville, Maryland; P. A. A. Loof of Wageningen, the Netherlands; and S. A. Sher of Riverside, California, kindly reviewed the introduction.

To the technical evaluators who carefully authenticated the content— Dr. M. W. Brzeski of Skierniewice, Poland; Mr. R. P. Esser of Gainesville, Florida; Dr. E. Geraert of Gent, Belgium; and Mr. B. E. Hopper of Ottawa, Canada, I extend my deepest appreciation. To Miss Gene M. Cooney, laboratory slave, who willingly, if not enthusiastically, spent countless hours recording and verifying data, I offer heartfelt thanks. Kudos are also tendered to Miss Gail A. Freybourg for her efforts, to Mrs. Sue Zambito for her careful correction of the data, and to Mrs. Wanda H. Leonard for the error-free typing of the manuscript.

An attempt has been made to construct this work in a comprehensible manner, yet devoid of superfluity. I hope that my interpretation of certain nomenclatorial actions has not led to over-simplification or, at worst, to actual error.

University of Florida
Citrus Experiment Station
Lake Alfred, Florida
June 20, 1966

ARMEN C. TARJAN

Table of Contents

Introduction

THIS WORK, as the title implies, supplements the original "Check List of Plant and Soil Nematodes" published in 1960. It seeks to present both new names and nomenclatorial changes of old names published from 1961 through 1965. It also corrects some errors in the original work. Two major publications which have contributed greatly to the present supplement are the 1961 book by A. H. Meyl, "Die freilebenden Erd- und Süsswassernematoden (Fadenwürmer)" and J. B. Goodey's 1963 revision of his father's "Soil and Fresh Water Nematodes."

As in the 1960 Check List, this Supplement does not attempt to present my opinion on what constitutes the correct name for any taxon; it merely lists chronologically the changes and additions to species names validly proposed under the International Rules of Zoological Nomenclature.

Also, as before, all names originally proposed as varieties or forms are regarded as belonging to the infrasubspecific category in accordance with the originator's designation. Hence, when such an infrasubspecific name is subsequently elevated to subspecies or species status, the name of the subsequent revisor replaces the name of the originator. This is in accordance with Article 10(b) in the 1961 edition of the Rules. Yet, Article 45(d)(i) states that before 1961 a name is determined as subspecific if the author "did not clearly state its rank." It is further claimed in section (e)(i) of the same article that "Before 1961, the use of the terms 'variety' or 'form' is not to be interpreted as an express statement of either subspecific or infrasubspecific rank." This implies that the original author of an infrasubspecific name, in addition to listing the appropriate infrasubspecific term, must have clearly stated somewhere in the article that the taxon was a variety, form, etc. Other than the difficulties imposed in determining whether the author fulfilled these requirements, particularly in a language unfamiliar to the reader, another problem exists. A rigid enforcement of this interpretation would create some confusion as illustrated by *Aphelenchus parietinus,* var. *micro-tubifer* f. *parvus* s.f. *informis; A. parietinus,* var. *microtubifer* f. *magnus* s.f. *informis;* and *A. parietinus,* var. *tubifer* f. *magnus* s.f. *informis,* which Micoletzky, 1922 regarded as different taxa, all assuming the name *A. parietinus informis.* Similar cases involve the terminal names *steineri* and *parvus* appearing in the nominal chains following *Dorylaimus carteri.* It is for these reasons that in the 1960 work, and again in this Supplement, the names are considered *in the rank designated by the original author.* Any nomenclatorial action by a subsequent reviewer can thus be effectively dealt with without confusion.

A supplement to a published work must be comprehensible and simple to use. With this view in mind, the present Supplement has been designed to use four symbols for introducing the new material. The symbols preceding each species name are:

A—which signifies that new information is added to a name appearing in the 1960 Check List.

C—meaning that some of the information in the original work is changed.

T—meaning that a species name in the 1960 work has had its gender and spelling changed and that the entire entry is transferred to a new alphabetical position within the 1960 work.

N—signifying that the entry is new and not in the 1960 book.

The symbol (*c*) will occasionally appear at the end of the last line in a column, and will indicate that the entry is continued to the next column.

In this Supplement, the centered page number refers to the paginal position in the 1960 Check List where the novel information belongs. When, in the 1960 work, an entry began on one page and extended to the next page, then the correction in the supplement refers to the page on which the entry began. Entries beginning with *A, C,* or *T* list the species name, directly followed by the original genus name (and sometimes the name of the author, when needed to definitely identify the taxon). Under these species names are listed in numerical progression, the changes to be made or, in the simplest form, merely the notation "Add:" with the material included in immediate juxtaposition. An entry preceded by *N* always lists only the species name on the first line, with the genus name and the other information directly below it. All other systems of presenting information are identical with those used in the 1960 work.

Keyed Explanation of Four Typical Entries

N^1—*bulbosus*[2]
Prismatolaimus[3] Milne, 1963 *1387*[4]
1387[5] syn: *Prismatolaimus dolichurus,*
var. *bulbosus* Daday, 1897

A^6—*carotae, Heterodera*[7]
1. Place asterisk before *Heterodera*[8]
2. Add: *valid name according to
Goodey, 1963 *1234*[9]

C,T^{10}—*coronata, Rhabditis*
1. Change species name to *coronatus*[11]
2. Transpose entire entry to immediately after *coronatus, Plectonchus*[12]

A,C,T^{13}—*italicus, Neotylenchus*[7]
1. Change species name to *italicum*[11]
2. Transpose entire entry to immediately after *italiae, Xiphinema*[12]
3. Add: *Scytaleum* (Meyl, 1954) Andrássy, 1961 *1088*[14]

1. Symbol indicating a new name not listed in the 1960 Check List
2. Specific name
3. Generic name followed by authority and date
4. Literature reference number in which the new name was proposed
5. Literature reference number in which the synonymy which follows was made
6. Symbol indicating that the information following is to be added to a name already appearing in the 1960 Check List
7. The scientific name of the nematode referred to in the previous note
8. Style used for indicating the placement of an asterisk before a genus name listed in the 1960 Check List
9. Style used for indicating the authority for current usage of a name
10. Symbols indicating a change in an entry appearing in the 1960 Check List, and transposition of the entry to a new alphabetical position resulting from change of gender in the species name
11. Style used for indicating a change in gender of a species name
12. Style used for indicating new alphabetical position of a transposed entry
13. Combination of symbols indicating the addition of new information to, the correction of some information in, and the transposition of an entry appearing in the 1960 Check List
14. A typical addition of a new combination to an established species name

xiii

List of Species

N—aberrans
Agmodorus Thorne, 1964 *1133*

A—aberrans, Anguillulina Altherr
1. Place asterisk before *Tylenchus*
2. Add: *Lelenchus* (Altherr, 1952) Baker, 1962 *784*
   *regarded as valid name by Goodey, 1963 *881*
   NOTE: placed in *species inquirendae* by Meyl, 1961 *1028*

A—aberrans, Cephalobus
Add: *Panagrolaimus* (Steiner, 1929) Goodey, 1963 *881*

N—aberrans
Criconemoides Jairajpuri & Siddiqi, 1963 *948*
Lobocriconema (Jairajpuri & Siddiqi, 1963) de Grisse & Loof, 1965 *891*

A,C—aberrans, Hoplolaimus
1. Change 1959 to 1960
2. Add: *Scutellonema* (Whitehead, 1960) Sher, 1961 *1065*

A—aberrans, Plectus
Add: NOTE: placed in *species inquirendae* by Maggenti, 1961 *1020*

A—aberrans, Psilenchus
Add: *881* = *Tylenchus* [*Filenchus*] *neoaberrans* Goodey, 1963
Basiria (Thorne, 1949) Siddiqi, 1963 *1085*

A—aberrans, Rhabditis
Add: NOTE: placed in *species inquirendae* by Meyl, 1961 *1028*, but regarded a valid species by Goodey, 1963 *881*

A—abieticolus, Ditylenchus
Add: *Neoditylenchus* (Rühm, 1956) Meyl, 1961 *1028*

A—abnormis, Cylindrolaimus
1. Place asterisk before *Cylindrolaimus*
2. Add: *881* syn: *Gymnolaimus exilis* of Goodey, 1951
   *valid genus according to Goodey, 1963 *881*

N—abrupticaudatus
Mononchus Altherr, 1960 *753*
Cobbonchus (Altherr, 1960) Goodey, 1963 *881*

N—acanthocini
Parasitorhabditis Lazarevskaja, 1961 *990a*

N—acarambates
Pelodera [*Coarctadera*] Poinar, 1965 *1043*

A—aciculus, Paratylenchus
1. Place asterisk before *Paratylenchus*
2. Add: *Gracilacus* (Brown, 1959) Raski, 1962 *1044*
   *valid genus according to Siddiqi & Goodey, 1964 *1103*

A—acris, Dorylaimus
Add: *Mesodorylaimus* (Thorne, 1939) Goodey, 1963 *881*

A—acris, Rhabditis
Add: NOTE: (2) placed in *species inquirendae* by Meyl, 1961 *1028*

N—acris
Tylencholaimellus Thorne, 1964 *1133*

A—acronea, Meloidogyne
Add: *984 Meloidogyne acronea* of Poghossian, 1960 = *Meloidogyne poghossianae* Kirjanova, 1963
Hypsoperine (Coetzee, 1956) Sledge & Golden, 1964 *1116*

1

A—acti, Tylenchorhynchus
Add: 1078 = Tylenchorhynchus capitatus Allen, 1955
NOTE: regarded a valid species by Hopper in Tarjan, 1964 1125

A—aculeatus, Cephalobus
Add: NOTE: placed in species inquirendae by Sanwal, 1960 1057

A—aculentus, Paratylenchus
1. Place asterisk before Paratylenchus
2. Add: Gracilacus (Brown, 1959) Raski, 1962 1044
*valid genus according to Siddiqi & Goodey, 1964 1103

A,C—acuminatus, Plectus
1. Delete note
2. Add: 1020 syn: Plectus communis Bütschli, 1873 in part Proteroplectus (Bastian, 1865) Paramonov, 1964 1040

PAGE 3

A—acuminatus, Pseudorhabditis
Add: Trilabiatus (Kreis, 1929) Goodey, 1963 881

N—acuminatus
Tylodorus Meagher, 1964 1026

N—acutis
Nordia Jairajpuri & Siddiqi, 1964 950
Enchodorella (Jairajpuri & Siddiqi, 1964) Siddiqi, 1964 1090a

A—acutocaudatus, Tylenchus
1. Place asterisk before 454
2. Add: *accepted as valid by numerous authors

A—acutus, Acrobeles
Add: Cervidellus (Kirjanova, 1951) Meyl, 1961 1028
Acrobeloides (Kirjanova, 1951) Goodey, 1963 881
NOTE: placed in species inquirendae by Meyl, 1961 1028

N—acutus
Nothotylenchus Khan, 1965 976

N—adalberti
Mesodorylaimus Andrássy, 1963 774

N—adamsi
Neocriconema Diab & Jenkins, 1965 845

N—adelaidensis
Dolichodorus Fisher, 1964 856

A—aderholdi, Aphelenchus
Add: NOTE: placed in species inquirendae by Goodey, 1960 876

N—adipatus
Eudorylaimus Brzeski, 1962 796

A—aequidentatus, Paradiplogaster
Add: NOTE: placed in species inquirendae by Goodey, 1963 881

A—aerivora, Diplogaster
Add: Mikoletzkya (Cobb in Merrill & Ford, 1916) Baker, 1962 784

N—aestuarius
Psilenchus Andrássy, 1962 771

N—afer
Eudorylaimus Andrássy, 1964 781

N—affinis
Discolaimus Loof, 1964 1001

N—affinis
Rotylenchoides Luc, 1960 1009

A—affinis, Tripyla
Add: 799 syn: Tripyla tatrica Stefánski, 1924

PAGE 4

N—afghanicus
Dorylaimus Andrássy, 1960 762

A,C,T—africana, Diplogasteroides
1. Change species name to africanus
2. Transpose to immediately after africanus, Actinolaimus
3. Place asterisk before Diplogasteroides
4. Add: *valid genus according to Massey, 1962 1024

2

C—*africana, Meloidogyne*
　Change 1959 to 1960

N—*africanum*
　Thornenema Andrássy, 1965 *781a*

A—*africanus, Tylenchus*
　1. Place asterisk before *Helicotylenchus*
　2. Add: *valid genus according to Sher, 1961 *1065*

N—*afzali*
　Longidorus Khan, 1964 *962*
　Paralongidorus (Khan, 1964) Siddiqi & Husain, 1965 *1106*

A—*agilior, Plectus*
　Add: NOTE: placed in *species inquirendae* by Maggenti, 1961 *1020*

A—*agilis, Diplogaster*
　Add: *Hemidiplogaster* (Skwarra, 1921) Goodey, 1963 *881*
　881 syn: *Diplogaster paulyi* Fuchs, 1933

A,C—*agilis, Dorylaimus*
　1. Delete asterisks and footnote
　2. Add: *Mesodorylaimus* (de Man, 1880) Goodey, 1963 *881*

N—*agri*
　Tylenchorhynchus Ferris, 1963 *855*

A,C—*agricola, Tylenchus*
　1. Delete asterisks and footnote
　2. Place asterisk before *Tylenchus* [*Aglenchus*]
　3. Add: *Aglenchus* (de Man, 1884) Meyl, 1961 *1028*
　　772 syn: *Tylenchus paragricola* Paetzold, 1958
　　*valid name according to Goodey, 1963 *881*

PAGE 5

N—*agropyronifloris*
　Anguina Norton, 1965 *1037*

N—*alata*
　Chronogaster Gerlach, 1954 *868*

A—*alatus, Tylenchus*
　Add: NOTE: placed in *species inquirendae* by Tarjan, 1964 *1125*

A—*albus, Diplogaster*
　Add: NOTE: (2) placed in *species inquirendae* by Meyl, 1961 *1028*

N—*alleni*
　Anatonchus Mulvey, 1961 *1031*

N—*alleni*
　Eudorylaimus Brzeski, 1962 *792*

N—*alleni*
　Pratylenchus Ferris, 1961 *854*

A—*allgeni, Dorylaimus*
　Add: *49b* syn: *Dorylaimus carieri* of Allgén, 1929 as entry directly under *Dorylaimus*

N—*allius*
　Trichodorus Jensen, 1963 *953*

A—*allocotus, Ditylenchus*
　Add: *881* = *Anguillula dipsaci* Kühn, 1857

PAGE 6

N—*alticolum*
　Criconema Colbran, 1965 *832b*

N—*amabilis*
　Qudsianema Jairajpuri, 1965 *941*

N—*amalgans*
　Tyleptus Thorne, 1964 *1133*

A—*amblycephalus, Paratylenchus*
　Add: *809 = *Paratylenchus nanus* Cobb, 1923
　　866 Paratylenchus amblycephalus Reuver, 1959 (in part) = *Paratylenchus neoamblycephalus* Geraert, 1965
　　*synonymy not recognized by Geraert, 1965 *866*

N—*americanum*
　Enchodorella Khan, 1964 *961*
　961 syn: *Longidorella parva* of Tarjan, 1953

A—*americanus, Diplogaster*
Add: *Mononchoides* (Steiner, 1930)
Goodey, 1963 *881*

N—*amiciae*
Anatonchus Coomans & Lima, 1965
839

N—*amorphus*
Criconemoides de Grisse in de Grisse
& Loof, 1965 *891*

A—*amphidiscatus, Plectus*
Add: NOTE: placed in *species inquirendae* by Maggenti, 1961 *1020*

N—*amphidium*
Axonchium Thorne, 1964 *1133*

N—*amphidius*
Proleptonchus Jairajpuri, 1964 *937*

A—*amplicolle, Axonchium*
Add: *938a* syn: *Discolaimim pakistanicum* Timm & Bhuiyan, 1963

A—*amsinckiae, Ditylenchus*
Add: *Anguina* (Filipjev & Schuurmans Stekhoven, 1941) Thorne,
1961 *1132*
881 = *Anguillula dipsaci* Kühn,
1857

A,C—*anceps, Paratylenchus*
1. Change footnote to: *valid genus
according to Siddiqi & Goodey, 1963
1103
2. Add: *Gracilacus* (Cobb, 1923)
Raski, 1962 *1044*
NOTE: placed in *species inquirendae*
by Tarjan, 1960 *1124*

A—*anchicoprophaga, Paroigolaimella*
Add: *Fictor* (Paramonov, 1952)
Goodey, 1963 *881*

N—*andinus*
Pratylenchus Lordello, Zamith, &
Boock, 1961 *1007*

N—*andrassyi*
Chronogaster Loof & Jairajpuri, 1965
1002

N—*andrassyi*
Diplogaster [*Eudiplogaster*] Timm,
1961 *1136*
Eudiplogaster (Timm, 1961) Timm,
1961 *1136*

N—*andrassyi*
Dorylaimellus Heyns, 1964 *906*

N—*anemones*
Trichodorus Loof, 1965 *1001b*

N—*angolense*
Enchodelium Andrássy, 1963 *772*

A—*angustalatus, Hoplolaimus*
Add: *1066* = *Tylenchorhynchus para-
robustus* Schuurmans Stekhoven &
Teunissen, 1938

A—*angustilaimus, Diplogaster*
Add: *Diplogasteritus* (Schuurmans
Stekhoven & Teunissen, 1938)
Goodey, 1963 *881*

N—*angustus*
Mesodorylaimus Andrássy, 1964 *781*

A—*annulata, Macroposthonia*
Add: *891* syn: *Criconemoides kirjanovae* Andrássy, 1962
891 Macroposthonia annulata of
Kischke, 1956 = *Hoplolaimus annulifer* de Man, 1921

A—*annulatum, Criconemoides*
Add: *891* = *Macroposthonia taylori* de
Grisse & Loof, 1965

C—*annulatus, Cephalobus*
1. Change note to: placed in *species
inquirendae* by Meyl, 1961 *1028*

A—*annulatus, Dorylaimus* Daday
1. Place asterisk in front of *Dorylaimus*
2. Add: *Mesodorylaimus* (Daday,
1905) Goodey, 1963 *881*
*valid species according to Loof,
1964 *1001*

N—*annulatus*
Ecphyadophoroides Corbett, 1964 *840*

N—*annulatus*
  Plectus Maggenti, 1961 *1020*
  Proteroplectus (Maggenti, 1961) Para-
  monov, 1964 *1040*

N—*annulatus*
  Tetylenchus Merny, 1964 *1027*

A,C—*annulifer, Hoplolaimus*
  1. Change species name to *annuli-
  ferum*
  2. Add: *Nothocriconema* (de Man,
  1921) de Grisse & Loof, 1965 *891*
  891 syn: *Criconema kirjanovae*
  Krall, 1963
  891 syn: *Macroposthonia annulata*
  of Kischke, 1956

A—*annulifer,* f. *hygrophilum, Criconema*
  Add: *Criconemoides* (Andrássy, 1952)
  Oostenbrink, 1960 *1038*
  881 = *Criconemoides hygrophilum*
  Goodey, 1963

A—*anomala, Rhabditis*
  Add: NOTE: placed in *species inquirendae* by Meyl, 1961 *1028* but regarded a valid species by Goodey,
  1963 *881*

PAGE 9

A,C—*antarcticus, Plectus*
  1. Delete asterisks and footnote
  2. Add: *1020* = *Plectus parietinus*
  Bastian, 1865

N—*antedontus*
  Iotonchus Mulvey, 1963 *1033*

N—*antipolitana*
  Criconemoides de Guiran, 1963 *892*
  Macroposthonia (de Guiran, 1963) de
  Grisse & Loof, 1965 *891*

N—*antricolus*
  Nothotylenchus Andrássy, 1961 *767*

A—*anura, Criconema*
  Add: *891* = *Hoplolaimus informe*
  Micoletzky, 1922

A—*aphodii, Cheilobus*
  Add: *Rhabditophanes* (Sachs, 1950)
  Baker, 1962 *784*

A—*aphodii, Diplogaster*
  1. Place asterisk before *Prosodontus*
  2. Add: *Eudiplogaster* (Bovien, 1937)
  Meyl, 1961 *1028*
  *valid genus according to Goodey,
  1963 *881*

N—*apiculus*
  Helicotylenchus Román, 1965 *1052*

N—*apitica*
  Doryschota Thorne, 1964 *1133*

A,C,T—*aquatica, Rhabditis*
  1. Change specific name to *aquaticus*
  2. Delete note
  3. Transpose entire entry to immediately below *aquaticus, Nygolaimus*
  4. Add: *Panagrolaimus* (Micoletzky,
  1913) Goodey, 1963 *881*

PAGE 10

N—*araucariae*
  Micoletzkya Rühm, 1965 *1055b*

N—*archium*
  Trichonchium Siddiqi & Khan, 1964
  1110
  1109 = *Basirotyleptus basiri* Jairajpuri,
  1964

A—*arctica, Parachromagasteriella*
  Add: NOTE: placed in *species inquirendae* by Goodey, 1963 *881*

N—*arcticus*
  Aphelenchoides Sanwal, 1965 *1061a*

N—*arcuata*
  Acrostichus Massey, 1962 *1024*
  Filipjevella (Massey, 1962) Laza-
  revskaja, 1965 *990c*

N—*arcuatum*
  Axonchium Thorne, 1964 *1133*

N—*arcuatus*
  Dorylaimoides Siddiqi, 1964 *1093*

N—*arcuatus*
  Tylenchus [*Tylenchus*] Siddiqi, 1963
  1083

N—*arcuicaudatum*
Discolaimlium Furstenberg & Heyns, 1965 *863a*

N—*arculatus*
Paratylenchus Luc & de Guiran, 1962 *1016*

N—*arcum*
Xiphinema Khan, 1964 *962*

A—*arenaria*, *Anguillula*
Add: *881* syn: *Meloidogyne arenaria arenaria* (Neal, 1889) Chitwood, 1949

A—*arenaria arenaria*, *Meloidogyne*
Add: *881* = *Anguillula arenaria* Neal, 1889

A—*arenaria thamesi*, *Meloidogyne*
Add: *881* = *Meloidogyne thamesi* in Chitwood et al., 1952

N—*arenarium*
Xiphinema Luc & Dalmasso, 1964 *1013*

N—*arenarius*
Dolichodorus Clark, 1963 *822*

N—*arenicola*
Anaplectus Killick, 1964 *980*

N—*arenicola*
Iotonchus Altherr, 1963 *756*

A,C—*arenicola*, *Tripyla*
1. Delete asterisks and footnote
2. On fifth & sixth lines under species name, change Altherr, 1952 *33* to Schuurmans Stekhoven, 1951 *590*
3. Place asterisk before *Trishcistoma*
4. Add: *Tripylina* (de Man, 1880) Brzeski, 1963 *800*
   *valid genus according to Brzeski, 1965 *807*

N—*arenicolus*
Mylonchulus Clark, 1961 *820*

N—*argentinica*
Stegelleta Andrássy, 1963 *774*

PAGE 11

N—*argentinus*
Mesodorylaimus Altherr, 1963 *756*

N—*armata*
Gaddinia Penso, 1938 *530*
Chiloplacus (Penso, 1938) Goodey, 1963 *881*
NOTE: placed in *species inquirendae* by Goodey, 1963 *881*

A—*armatus*, *Diplogaster*
Add: *Fictor* (Hofmänner, 1913) Goodey, 1963 *881*

A,C—*armatus*, *Plectus*
1. Delete asterisks and footnote
2. Add: *Proteroplectus* (Bütschli, 1873) Paramonov, 1964 *1040*
   NOTE: placed in *species inquirendae* by Meyl, 1961 *1028*

N—*armeniaca*
Meloidodera Poghossian, 1960 *1041*

N—*artiellia*
Meloidogyne Franklin, 1961 *860*

A—*asiatica*, *Tripyla*
Add: NOTE: placed in *species inquirendae* by Brzeski, 1964 *806*

A—*assimilis*, *Plectus*
Add: *Proteroplectus* (Bütschli, 1873) Paramonov, 1964 *1040*

N—*asterocaudatus*
Aphelenchoides Das, 1960 *842*

A—*asymmetrica*, *Diplogaster*
Add: *Fictor* (Steiner, 1928) Goodey, 1963 *881*

N—*asymmetricus*
Nygolaimus Andrássy, 1962 *770*

A—*ateri*, *Parasitaphelenchus*
Add: *876* = *Tylenchus uncinatus* Fuchs, 1929

A—*atratus*, *Dorylaimus*
Add: NOTE: placed in *species inquirendae* by Meyl, 1961 *1028*

PAGE 12

N—*attenuatus*
Longidorus Hooper, 1961 *909*

N—*attorodorum*
Xiphinema Luc, 1961 *1010*
1010 syn: *Xiphinema campinense* of Luc, 1957

A—*audriellus, Paratylenchus*
1. Place asterisk before *Paratylenchus*
2. Add: *Gracilacus* (Brown, 1959) Raski, 1962 *1044*
*valid genus according to Siddiqi & Goodey, 1964 *1103*

N—*australe*
Criconema Colbran, 1963 *832*

N—*australe*
Doryllium Grandison, 1964 *882*

N—*australis*
Cobbonchus Clark, 1963 *826*

A—*australis, Diplogaster*
Add: NOTE: placed in *species inquirendae* by Goodey, 1963 *881*

A—*australis, Prismatolaimus*
1. Place asterisk before *Prismatolaimus*
2. Add: *valid species according to Milne, 1963 *1029*

A—*austriacus, Diplogasteritus*
1. Place asterisk before *Diplogasteritus*
2. Add: *valid genus according to Meyl, 1961 *1028*

A—*autographi, Ditylenchus*
Add: *Neoditylenchus* (Rühm, 1956) Meyl, 1961 *1028*

A—*autographi, Parasitaphelenchus*
Add: NOTE: placed in *species inquirendae* by Goodey, 1960 *876*

A—*avenae, Aphelenchus*
Add: 876 syn: *Tylenchus cylindricaudatus* Cobb in Steiner, 1926
876 syn: *Aphelenchus macrobolbus* Steiner, 1942
879 syn: *Paraphelenchus micoletzkyi* Steiner, 1941 (*c*)

879 syn: *Metaphelenchus rhopalocercus* Steiner, 1943

A—*avenae, Heterodera*
1. Place asterisk before *Heterodera*
2. Add: *valid name according to Goodey, 1963 *881*

PAGE 13

A—*axei, Pelodera*
881 syn: *Rhabditis macrocera* Kreis & Faust, 1933
881 syn: *Rhabditis tricincta* Paesler, 1946
881 syn: *Rhabditella multipara* Li, 1951

A,C—*axeste, Criconemoides*
1. Change *axeste* to *axestus*
2. Add: *Macroposthonia* (Fassuliotis & Williamson, 1959) de Grisse & Loof, 1965 *891*

N—*bakeri*
Bursaphelenchus Rühm, 1964 *1055a*
1055a syn: *Aphelenchoides* [*Bursaphelenchus*] *sexdentati* Rühm, 1960

N—*bakeri*
Criconema Wu, 1964 *1158*
Bakernema Wu, 1964 *1157*

N—*bakeri*
Criconemoides Wu, 1965 *1160*
Macroposthonia (Wu, 1965) de Grisse & Loof, 1965 *891*

N—*bakeri*
Pelodera Rühm, 1964 *1055a*

N—*bakeri*
Xiphinema Williams, 1961 *1151*

N—*baldum*
Axonchium Thorne, 1964 *1133*

N—*bambesae*
Dorylaimellus de Coninck, 1962 *833*

A—*bandelieri, Diplogaster*
Add: NOTE: placed in *species inquirendae* by Goodey, 1963 *881*

7

basidontus

N—*basidontus*
Iotonchus Clark, 1961 *816*

N—*basilgoodeyi*
Xiphinema Coomans, 1965 *836*

N—*basili*
Criconemoides Jairajpuri, 1964 *930*
930 syn: *Criconemoides goodeyi* Jairajpuri, 1964
Macroposthonia (Jairajpuri, 1964) de Grisse & Loof, 1965 *891*

N—*basili*
Paraphelenchus Das, 1960 *842*

N—*basilogoodeyi*
Heterocephalobus Brzeski, 1961 *788*

N—*basiri*
Basirotyleptus Jairajpuri, 1964 *935*
1109 syn: *Trichonchium archium* Siddiqi & Khan, 1964

N—*basiri*
Dorylaimellus Jairajpuri, 1965 *942*

N—*basiri*
Nothotylenchus Khan, 1965 *976*

PAGE 14

A—*bastiani, Mononchus*
Add: *815* = *Oncholaimus muscorum* Dujardin, 1845

A,C—*bastiani*, var. *longicaudatus, Dorylaimus*
1. Delete asterisks and footnote
2. Add: *1028* = *Dorylaimus bastianoides* Meyl, 1961

N—*bastianoides*
Dorylaimus Meyl, 1961 *1028*
1028 syn: *Dorylaimus bastiani* var. *longicaudatus* Daday, 1894

A—*bathybius, Mononchus*
Add: NOTE: placed in *species inquirendae* by Mulvey, 1963 *1033*

A—*beaumonti, Dorylaimus*
Add: NOTE: placed in *species inquirendae* by Meyl, 1961 *1028*

bicornis

A—*behningi, Tylenchorhynchus*
Add: *Hirschmannia* (Micoletzky, 1923) Luc & Goodey, 1962 *1014*
Hirschmanniella (Micoletzky, 1923) Luc & Goodey, 1964 *1015*
NOTE: placed in *species inquirendae* by Luc & Goodey, 1962 *1014*

A—*belgicae, Plectus*
1. Delete asterisks and footnote
2. Add: *1020* = *Plectus parvus* Bastian, 1865
NOTE: placed in *species inquirendae* by Meyl, 1961 *1028*

A—*beljaevae, Criconema*
Add: *891* = *Iota simile* Cobb, 1918

A—*beljaevae, Hexatylus*
Add: *Neotylenchus* (Atakhanov, 1958) Andrássy, 1961 *767*

N—*bengalensis*
Rhabditis Inglis & Coles, 1961 *922*
922 syn: *Rhabditis* [*Choriorhabditis*] *marina*, var. *bengalensis* Timm, 1956

A—*berwigi, Diplogasteroides*
Add: *Rhabdontolaimus* (Rühm, 1959) Meyl, 1961 *1028*

PAGE 15

N—*beryllus*
Paralongidorus Siddiqi & Husain, 1965 *1106*

N—*bibigulae*
Chiloplacus Erzhanov, 1964 *852a*

N—*bicaudatus*
Pratylenchus Meyl, 1961 *1028*
1028 syn: *Pratylenchus pratensis*, var. *bicaudatus* Meyl, 1954

A—*bicornis, Diplogaster*
Add: *Koerneria* (Rahm, 1928) Goodey, 1963 *881*

A—*bicornis, Rhabditis*
Add: *Diploscapter* (Zimmermann, 1898) Goodey, 1963 *881*

8

bifasciatus

N—bifasciatus
Tylenchorhynchus Andrássy, 1961 766a

A—biformis, Hemicriconemoides
Add: Hemicycliophora (Chitwood & Birchfield, 1957) Goodey, 1963 881

N—birchfieldi
Hemicriconemoides Edward, Misra, & Singh, 1965 852

N—birketi
Actinolaimus Altherr, 1960 753

A—biroi var. zeylandicus, Dorylaimus
Add: 881 = Dorylaimus zeylandicus Goodey, 1963

PAGE 16

N—bisexualis
Swangeria Hopper, 1961 914

A—bisimilis, Acrobeles
Add: Chiloplacus (Thorne, 1925) Goodey, 1963 881

A—blaberum, Rotylenchus
Add: 1067 = Hoplolaimus bradys Steiner & LeHew, 1933

A—bodamicus, Diplogaster
Add: NOTE: placed in species inquirendae by Goodey, 1963 881

A—boettgeri, Criconemoides
Add: Criconema (Meyl, 1954) de Grisse & Loof, 1965 891
NOTE: placed in species inquirendae by Siddiqi & Goodey, 1964 1103

A—bogdanovikatjkovi, Anguillulina
Add: Tylenchorhynchus (Kirjanova, 1941) Loof, 1959 391ab

N—bombilectoides
Eudorylaimus Altherr, 1965 757a

N—bombilectus
Eudorylaimus Andrássy, 1962 770

A—bonus, Acrobeles
Add: 1028 = Cephalobus [Acrobeles] propinquus de Man, 1921
Cervidellus (Kirjanova, 1951) Goodey, 1963 881

bradys

A—boocki, Rotylenchus
Add: 1065 = Rotylenchus brachyurum Steiner, 1938

N—borealis
Rotylenchulus, Loof & Oostenbrink, 1962 1003

N—borinquensis
Helicotylenchus Román, 1965 1052

N—borneoensis
Trichodorus Hooper, 1962 910

A—brachycephalus, Aphelenchoides
Add: Laimaphelenchus (Thorne, 1935) Massey, 1956 1023
Ektaphelenchus (Thorne, 1935) Goodey, 1960 876

PAGE 17

A—brachyuris, Mononchus
Add: 1030 Mononchus brachyuris (male) of de Man, 1876 and (female) of de Man, 1884 = Mononchus [Mylonchulus] sigmaturus Cobb, 1917

PAGE 18

A—brachyuroides, Mononchus
Add: Granonchulus (Micoletzky, 1925) Mulvey, 1963 1034

A—brachyurum, Rotylenchus
Add: 1065 syn: Rotylenchus coheni Goodey, 1952
1065 syn: Rotylenchus boocki Lordello, 1957

A—brachyurus, Criconemoides
1. Place asterisk before Hemicriconemoides
2. Add: Hemicycliophora (Loos, 1949) Goodey, 1963 881
*valid genus according to Siddiqi & Goodey, 1964 1103

A—brachyurus, Tylenchus
Add: 993 syn: Pratylenchus steineri Lordello, Zamith & Boock, 1954

A—bradys, Hoplolaimus
Add: 1067 syn: Rotylenchus blaberus Steiner, 1937 (c)

9

1067 syn: *Scutellonema dioscorea* Lordello, 1959

A—*brakenhoffi, Judonchulus*
Add: NOTE: placed in *species inquirendae* by Mulvey, 1963 *1034*

A—*brasilica, Oigolaimella*
Add: NOTE: placed in *species inquirendae* by Goodey, 1963 *881*

A—*brassicae, Rhabditis*
Add: NOTE: placed in *species inquirendae* by Meyl, 1961 *1028* but regarded as valid species by Goodey, 1963 *881*

N—*brassicae*
Tylenchorhynchus Siddiqi, 1961 *1078*

PAGE 19

N—*brevicauda*
Cephalobus Penso, 1938 *530*

A—*brevicauda, Diplogaster*
Add: NOTE: placed in *species inquirendae* by Goodey, 1963 *881*

A—*brevicauda, Diplogasteroides*
Add: NOTE: placed in *species inquirendae* by Goodey, 1963 *881*

A—*brevicauda, Loxolaimus*
Add: *Diplogaster* (Schuurmans Stekhoven, 1951) Baker, 1962 *784*
NOTE: placed in *species inquirendae* by Goodey, 1963 *881*

N—*brevicaudatum*
Criconema Siddiqi, 1961 *1077*
Mesocriconema (Siddiqi, 1961) Andrássy, 1965 *781b*

A,C,T—*brevicaudatum, Xiphinema*
1. Change species name to *brevicaudatus*
2. Transpose entire entry to immediately after *brevicaudatus, Tylenchorhynchus*
3. Add: *Longidorus* (Schuurmans Stekhoven, 1951) Thorne, 1961 *1132*
NOTE: placed in *species inquirendae* by Luc & Tarjan, 1963 *1019*

N—*brevicaudatus*
Aphelenchoides Das, 1960 *842*

A,C—*brevicaudatus, Cephalobus*
1. Delete asterisks and footnote
2. Add: *Cephalobus* [*Cephalobus*] Zimmermann, 1898 *786*

A—*brevicaudatus, Diplogaster*
Add: *Diplogasteritus* (Schuurmans Stekhoven & Teunissen, 1938) Goodey, 1963 *881*

A—*brevicaudatus, Discomyctus*
Add: *995* syn: *Dorylaimellus mirabilis* Thorne, 1939
945 = *Tylenchus mirabilis* Bütschli, 1873

A—*brevicaudatus, Hexatylus*
Add: *1028* = *Hexatylus viviparus* Goodey, 1926

N—*brevicaudatus*
Prismatolaimus Andrássy, 1960 *761*
761 syn: *Prismatolaimus dolichurus,* var. *brevicaudatus* Wu & Hoeppli, 1929

N—*brevicaudatus*
Rotylenchus Colbran, 1962 *831*

N—*brevicercus*
Pratylenchus Das, 1960 *842*

N—*brevicolle*
Xiphinema Lordello & da Costa, 1961 *1004b*

N—*brevidens*
Dorylaimoides Thorne, 1964 *1133*

N—*breviglans*
Rotylenchus Sher, 1965 *1071*

N—*brevihastus*
Paratylenchus Wu, 1962 *1155*
809 = *Paratylenchus microdorus* Andrássy, 1959

N—*brevilineatus*
Tylenchorhynchus Williams, 1960 *1147*
1086 syn: *Tylenchorhynchus indicus* Siddiqi, 1961

N—*brevionchus*
Aphelenchoides Das, 1960 *842*

PAGE 20

A—*brigdammensis, Dorylaimus*
Add: *Prodorylaimus* (de Man, 1876)
Goodey, 1963 *881*

N—*broadbalkiensis*
Helicotylenchus Yuen, 1964 *1162*

A—*browni, Tylenchus*
Add: NOTE: (2) reinstated as valid
species by Andrássy, 1960 *761,*
but regarded of dubious standing
by Goodey, 1963 *881*

N—*browni*
Zygotylenchus Siddiqi, 1963 *1084*
1129 = *Pratylenchoides guevarai* Tobar Jiménez, 1963

A—*brunettii, Procephalobus*
Add: *Panagrolaimus* (Marinari, 1957)
Meyl, 1961 *1028*

A—*bryophilum, Tylencholaimus*
1. Place asterisk before *Tylencholaimus*
2. Add: *valid genus according to
Clark, 1961 *815b*

N—*bryophilus*
Amphidelus Andrássy, 1961 *766*
766 syn: *Amphidelus elegans,* f. *bryophilus* Andrássy, 1952

N—*bryophilus*
Limonchulus Andrássy, 1963 *772*

A,C—*bryophilus, Tylenchus*
1. Delete asterisks and footnote
2. Place asterisk before *Tylenchus*
[*Aglenchus*]
3. Add: *Aglenchus* (Steiner, 1914)
Meyl, 1961 *1028*
*valid name according to Goodey,
1963 *881*

PAGE 21

N—*bucculentus*
Aetholaimus Williams, 1962 *1148*

A—*bucharicus, Anguillulina*
Add: NOTE: placed in *species inquirendae* by Tarjan, 1964 *1125*

A—*buchneri, Cephalobus*
1. Place asterisk before *Cephalobus*
2. Add: *Cephalobus* [*Cephalobus*]
Meyl, 1953 *786*
*valid name according to Meyl,
1961 *1028*

N—*buckleyi*
Nothotylenchus Das, 1960 *842*

A—*bucrius, Trichodorus*
Add: *1081* = *Trichodorus porosus* Allen, 1957

A—*buetschlii, Cephalobus*
Add: *881 Acrobeloides buetschlii* of
Steiner & Buhrer, 1933 = *Acrobe-
loides recurvatus* Goodey, 1963

A—*buetschlii, Diplogaster*
Add: *881* syn: *Diplogaster* [*Mikoletzkya*] *buetschlii buetschlii* Fuchs,
1915

881 syn: *Diplogaster* [*Mikoletzkya*]
buetschlii acunniati Rühm, 1954
881 syn: *Diplogaster buetschlii,* var.
acuminatus Micoletzky, 1922
881 syn: *Fuchsia buetschlii acuminati* Rühm, 1956
Mikoletzkya (Fuchs, 1915) Baker,
1962 *784*

A—*buetschlii acuminati, Fuchsia*
Add: *Mikoletzkya* (Rühm, 1956)
Baker, 1962 *784*
881 = *Diplogaster buetschlii* Fuchs,
1915

A—*buetschlii acunniati, Diplogaster*
Add: *881* = *Diplogaster buetschlii*
Fuchs, 1915

A—*buetschlii buetschlii, Diplogaster*
Add: *881* = *Diplogaster buetschlii*
Fuchs, 1915

A—*buetschlii,* var. *acuminatus, Diplogas-
ter*
Add: *881* = *Diplogaster buetschlii*
Fuchs, 1915

A—*buetschlii*, var. *conilabiatus*, *Acrobeloides*
Add: *1028* = *Acrobeloides conilabiatus* Meyl, 1961

A—*bukowinensis, Paratylenchus*
Add: *866* syn: *Paratylenchus nanus* Cobb, 1923

PAGE 22

A—*bulbifera, Monhystera*
Add: NOTE: placed in *species inquirendae* by Meyl, 1961 *1028*

A—*bulbifera, Tripyla*
Add: NOTE: placed in *species inquirendae* by Brzeski, 1964 *806*

A,C—*bulbiferus, Dorylaimus*
1. Change species name to *bulbiferum*
2. Add *Discolaimoides* (Cobb, 1906) Heyns, 1963 *902*
Discolaimium (Cobb, 1906) Timm & Bhuiyan, 1963 *1143*
*valid genus according to Loof, 1964 *1001*

N—*bulbosus*
Prismatolaimus Milne, 1963 *1029*
1029 syn: *Prismatolaimus dolichurus,* var. *bulbosus* Daday, 1897

N—*bulbosus*
Tarjania Brzeski & Szczygiel, 1961 *808*
Dorylaimoides (Brzeski & Szczygiel, 1961) Szczygiel, 1965 *1123*

A—*bulgaricum, Triplonchium*
1. Place 1958 after Andrássy
2. Add: *Tylolaimophorus* (Andrássy, 1958) Goodey, 1963 *881*

N—*bulgariensis*
Xiphinema Stoianov, 1964 *1117*

C—*bursifer, Tylenchorhynchus*
change 1959 to 1960

A—*buxophilus, Rotylenchus*
1. Place asterisk before *Rotylenchus*
2. Add: *1071* syn: *Rotylenchus sheri* Jairajpuri, 1964
*valid genus according to Sher, 1961 *1065*

N—*bwana*
Afrodorylaimus Andrássy, 1964 *781*

A—*cacti, Heterodera*
1. Place asterisk before *Heterodera*
2. Add: *valid name according to Goodey, 1963 *881*

N—*caespiticola*
Longidorus Hooper, 1961 *909*

A—*cafeicola, Tylenchus*
Add: NOTE: believed to be a *Ditylenchus* by Goodey, 1963 *881* but description is too meager

N—*caffrae*
Dorylaimellus Kruger, 1965 *989*

N—*cairnsi*
Helicotylenchus Waseem, 1961 *1145*

N—*californicus*
Hoplolaimus Sher, 1963 *1066*

N—*californicus*
Miconchus Mulvey, 1962 *1032*

A—*callosus, Dorylaimus*
Add: *Mesodorylaimus* (Skwarra, 1921) Goodey, 1963 *881*

N—*calvus*
Rotylenchus Sher, 1965 *1071*

A—*campbelli, Mononchus*
1. Place double asterisk before *49d*
2. Add: **Invalid synonymy according to Clark, 1963 *826*
NOTE: placed in *species inquirendae* by Clark, 1960 *814*, but reinstated as valid species by Clark, 1963 *826*

A—*campinense, Xiphinema*
Add: *1010 Xiphinema campinense* of Luc, 1957 = *Xiphinema attorodorum* Luc, 1961
1019 = *Xiphinema elongatum* Schuurmans Stekhoven & Teunissen, 1938

PAGE 23

N—*canadensis*
Helicotylenchus Waseem, 1961 *1145*

N—*canadensis*
   Macrolaimus Sanwal, 1960 *1057*

N—*candidus*
   Amphidelus Siddiqi & Basir, 1965 *1100*

N—*capitata*
   Mesorhabditis Loof, 1964 *1001*

N—*capitatus*
   Dorylaimellus Siddiqi, 1964 *1092a*

N—*capitatus*
   Gracilacus Adams & Eichenmuller, 1962 *750*
   Paratylenchus (Adams & Eichenmuller, 1962) Siddiqi & Goodey, 1964 *1103*
   866 = *Paratylenchus marylandicus* Jenkins, 1960

A—*capitatus, Tylenchorhynchus*
   Add: *1078 syn: *Tylenchorhynchus acti* Hopper, 1959
   *invalid synonymy according to Hopper in Tarjan, 1964 *1125*

A—*caprifici, Anguillula*
   1. Place asterisk before *Schistonchus*
   2. Add: *Aphelenchoides* (Gasparrini, 1864) Filipjev, 1934 *876*
   *valid genus according to Sanwal, 1961 *1060*

N—*capsici*
   Aorolaimus Jiménez Millán, Arias Delgado & Fijo, 1964 *954*

N—*captivitatis*
   Nygolaimellus Andrássy, 1962 *770*

N—*caribensis*
   Helicotylenchus Román, 1965 *1052*

A—*carinthiacus, Rhabditolaimus*
   Add: NOTE: put in subgenus *Amphidiplogasteroides* by Rühm, 1950 in his unpublished thesis, according to Körner, 1954

A—*caromatus, Anguillulina*
   Add: NOTE: placed in *species inquirendae* by Tarjan, 1964 *1125*

A—*carotae, Heterodera*
   1. Place asterisk before *Heterodera*
   2. Add: *valid name according to Goodey, 1963 *881*

A—*carteri, Dorylaimus*
   Add: *496 Dorylaimus carteri* of Allgén, 1929 = *Dorylaimus allgeni* Andrássy, 1958 as sixth entry under species name

PAGE 25

N—*castellanensis*
   Trichodorus Arias Delgado, Jiménez Millán & López Pedregal, 1965 *782*

N—*caudaphasmidius*
   Rotylenchus Sher, 1965 *1071*

N—*caudata*
   Diphtherophora Ivanova, 1958 *923*

N—*caudatus*
   Nygellus Jairajpuri, 1964 *936*

C—*caussaneli, Rhabditis*
   At the end of the first entry under the species name change 1900 *445* to 1899 *444*

N—*cavenessi*
   Scutellonema Sher, 1964 *1067*

N—*cedari*
   Xenonchium Siddiqi & Khan, 1964 *1108*

N—*cedarus*
   Trichodorus Yokoo, 1964 *1160d*

N—*celeris*
   Seinura Hechler in Hechler & Taylor, 1965, *897*

N—*celetum*
   Criconema Wu, 1960 *1153*

PAGE 26

A—*cembraei, Parasitorhabditis*
   Add: NOTE: placed in *species inquirendae* by Goodey, 1963 *881*

N—*cephalus*
Dorylaimellus Jairajpuri, 1964 *936*

A—*chappuisi, Dorylaimus*
Add: NOTE: placed in *species inquirendae* by Goodey, 1963 *881*

N—*chararasi*
Panagrolaimus Rühm in Rühm & Chararas, 1957 *1056*

N—*charis*
Meloidodera Hopper, 1960 *913*

N—*chauliodus*
Cobbonchus Clark, 1961 *817*

N—*chelatus*
Acrobeles Thomas & Allen, 1965 *1131*

A—*chengmohliangi, Plectus*
Add: *761* = *Plectus   longicaudatus*
Bütschli, 1873
NOTE: placed in *species inquirendae* by Maggenti, 1961 *1020*

A—*chitwoodi, Aphelenchoides*
Add: *Bursaphelenchus* (Rühm, 1956) Goodey, 1960 *876*

N—*chitwoodi*
Hemicriconemoides Esser, 1960 *853*
Hemicycliophora   (Esser,   1960)
Goodey, 1963 *881*
*valid genus according to Siddiqi & Goodey, 1964 *1103*

A,C—*chitwoodi, Rhabditis*
1. In the third entry under the species name, change Hirschmann, 1952 to: of Osche, 1952
2. Add: *1028* syn: *Rhabditis* [*Rhabditis*] *limicola* Hirschmann, 1952 and [*Pelodera*] directly after *Pelodera* in the second entry under the species name.

PAGE 27

N—*chowdhuri*
Paurodontus Husain & Khan, 1965 *915*

N—*christenseni*
Diphtherophora Husain, Khan & s'Jacob, 1965 *921*

A—*christiei, Rotylenchus*
Add: *Peltamigratus* (Golden & Taylor, 1956) Sher, 1964 *1068*

N—*christiei*
Seinura Goodey, 1960 *876*
876 syn: *Aphelenchoides tenuicaudatus* of Christie, 1939
896 = *Aphelenchus tenuicaudatus* de Man, 1895

A—*ciliatus, Acrobeles*
Add: *761* syn: *Acrobeles sinensis* Kreis, 1930
761 syn: *Acrobeles complexus* Thorne, 1925

A—*cinctus, Dorylaimus*
Add: †*Eudorylaimus* (Cobb in Thorne & Swanger, 1936) Andrássy, 1959 *50d*

N—*cinctus*
Tylencholaimellus Orr & Dickerson, 1965 *1039*

N—*circulifer*
Eudorylaimus Loof, 1961 *995*
995 syn: *Dorylaimus intermedius* of Thorne & Swanger, 1936

A—*cirratus, Plectus*
Add: *798* syn: *Plectus tenuis* of Kozlowska, 1962 in part

A—*citri, Aphelenchoides*
1. Place asterisk before *Aphelenchoides*
2. Add: *Seinura* (Andrássy, 1957) Goodey, 1960 *876*
*valid genus according to Meyl, 1961 *1028*

A—*citri, Criconemoides*
Add: *1001* = *Criconemoides sphaerocephalum* Taylor, 1936
NOTE: Andrássy, 1965 *781b* claims that only *C. citri* of Siddiqi, 1961 (not Steiner, 1949) is a synonym of *C. sphaerocephalum.*

N—*citri*
Diphtherophora Husain, Khan & s'Jacob, 1965 *921*

14

A—citri, Macrolaimus
Add: NOTE: placed in *species inqui-rendae* by Sanwal, 1960 *1057*

A—citri, Xiphinema
Add: *Longidorus* (Siddiqi, 1959) Thorne, 1961 *1132*
Paralongidorus (Siddiqi, 1959) Siddiqi, Hooper & Khan, 1963 *1104*

N—citricola
Criconemoides Siddiqi, 1965 *1095*

N—clarus
Proleptonchus Timm, 1964 *1140*

A—clausii, Rhabditis
Add: NOTE: placed in *species inqui-rendae* by Goodey, 1963 *881*

PAGE 28

N—clavatum
Xiphinema Heyns, 1965 *908*

N—clavatus
Dorylaimellus Thorne, 1964 *1133*

A,C,T—clavicaudatus, Dorylaimellus
1. Change species name to *clavi-caudata*
2. Transpose entire entry to immediately below *clavatus, Nygellus*
3. Add: *Belondira* (Williams, 1958) Andrássy, 1963 *774*

N—clavicaudatus
Tylenchorhynchus Seinhorst, 1963 *1064*

A,C—clavicaudatus, Tylenchus
1. Delete asterisks and footnote
2. Place asterisk before *Psilenchus*
3. Add: NOTE: regarded in doubtful position by Siddiqi, 1963 *1085*

A—clavus, Diplogaster
Add: NOTE: placed in *species inqui-rendae* by Meyl, 1961 *1028*

N—closelongatus
Longidorus Stoianov, 1964 *1117*

A—cobbi, Iota
Add: *1103* syn: *Criconema cobbi*, f. *duplex* deConinck, 1945
1103 syn: *Criconema cobbi*, f. *multiplex* deConinck, 1945

PAGE 29

A—cobbi, Tylenchus
Add: *876* = *Tylenchus gracilis* Cobb, 1888

A—cobbi, f. duplex, Criconema
Add: *1103* = *Iota cobbi* Micoletzky, 1925

A—cobbi, f. multiplex, Criconema
Add: *1103* = *Iota cobbi* Micoletzky, 1925

A—cobbi, f. typica, Criconema
Add: NOTE: with the synonymization of the two preceding forms, the form designation *"typica"* becomes unnecessary.

A—cocophillus, Criconemoides
1. Place asterisk before *Hemicricone-moides*
2. Add: *Hemicycliophora* (Loos, 1949) Goodey, 1963 *881*
*valid genus according to Siddiqi & Goodey, 1964 *1103*

A,C—cocophilus, Aphelenchus
1. Delete asterisks and footnote
2. Add: *Rhadinaphelenchus* (Cobb, 1919) Goodey, 1960 *875*

A—coffeae, Aphelenchus Noack
Add: NOTE: (2) placed in *species in-quirendae* by Goodey, 1960 *876*

A—coffeae, Aphelenchus Zimmermann
Add: NOTE: (2) regarded a valid species by Sanwal, 1961 *1060*

N—coffeae
Tylenchorhynchus Siddiqi & Basir, 1959 *1099*
NOTE: placed in *species inquirendae* by Tarjan, 1964 *1125*

15

A—*coffeae, Tylenchus*
    Add: *993* syn: *Tylenchus* [*Chitinotylenchus*] sp. of Schneider, 1938
    993 syn: *Pratylenchus pratensis* of Yokoo, 1956
    993 syn: *Pratylenchus coffeae* of Loos, 1953 = *Pratylenchus loosi* Loof, 1960

A—*coffeae*, var. *brevicauda, Tylenchus*
    Add: NOTE: placed in *species inquirendae* by Loof, 1960 *993*

N—*coffeicola*
    Meloidogyne Lordello & Zamith, 1960 *1006*
    Meloidodera (Lordello & Zamith, 1960) Kirjanova, 1963 *984*

A—*coheni, Rotylenchus*
    Add: *1065* = *Rotylenchus brachyurum* Steiner, 1938

PAGE 30

N—*colobocercus*
    Diplenteron Andrássy, 1964 *779*

N—*colourus*
    Ironus Meyl, 1961 *1028*
    1028 syn: *Ironus ignavus,* var. *colourus* Steiner, 1919

N—*columbus*
    Hoplolaimus Sher, 1963 *1066*

N—*communis*
    Hemicriconemoides Edward & Misra, 1964 *851*

A—*communis, Plectus*
    Add: *1020* = *Plectus parvus* Bastian, 1865 in part
    1020 = *Plectus acuminatus* Bastian, 1865 in part

N—*complexa*
    Criconemoides Jairajpuri, 1964 *938*
    Macroposthonia (Jairajpuri, 1964) de Grisse & Loof, 1965 *891*

A—*complexus, Acrobeles*
    Add: *761* = *Acrobeles ciliatus* Linstow, 1877

N—*composticola*
    Mononchus Clark, 1960 *814*

N—*concavus*
    Helicotylenchus Román, 1961 *1050*

N—*concolor*
    Acrostichus Massey, 1962 *1024*
    Filipjevella (Massey, 1962) Lazarevskaja, 1965 *990c*

N—*concolor*
    Panagrolaimus Massey, 1964 *1025a*

A—*condamni, Dorylaimus*
    Add: NOTE: placed in *species inquirendae* by Meyl, 1961 *1028*

N—*congoensis*
    Drilocephalobus Coomans & Goodey, 1965 *838*

A—*congolense, Criconema*
    Add: *781b* = *Iota peruensis* Cobb, 1924
    NOTE: placed in *species inquirendae* by Siddiqi & Goodey, 1964 *1103* and in *incertae sedis* by de Grisse & Loof, 1965 *891*

A—*conicaudatum, Trischistoma*
    Add: *Tripyla* (Schuurmans Stekhoven, 1951) Goodey, 1963 *881*

N—*conilabiatus*
    Acrobeloides Meyl, 1961 *1028*
    1028 syn: *Acrobeloides buetschlii,* var. *conilabiatus* Meyl, 1953

A—*conjunctus, Parasitaphelenchus*
    Add: *784 Aphelenchoides* [*Bursaphelenchus*] *conjunctus* of Rühm, 1956 and *Bursaphelenchus conjunctus* of Goodey, 1960 = *Bursaphelenchus ruehmi* Baker, 1962
    NOTE: placed in *species inquirendae* by Goodey, 1960 *876* and 1963 *881*, but regarded as valid species by Meyl, 1961 *1028*

PAGE 31

A,C—*consobrinus, Diplogaster*
    1. Delete asterisks and footnote (*c*)

16

consobrinus

2. Add: *Diplogastrellus* (de Man, 1920) Meyl, 1961 *1028*
Acrostichus (de Man, 1920) Massey, 1962 *1024*

A—*consobrinus*, var. *austriacus*, *Diplogaster*
Add: *Acrostichus* (Fuchs, 1938) Massey, 1962 *1024*

N—*contractus*
Tylenchorhynchus Loof, 1964 *1001*

N—*conurum*
Xiphinema Siddiqi, 1964 *1094*

A—*conurus*, *Aphelenchoides*
Add: *Bursaphelenchus* (Steiner, 1932) Goodey, 1960 *876*

A—*conurus*, *Dorylaimus*
Add: *Mesodorylaimus* (Thorne, 1939) Goodey, 1963 *881*

N—*convallariae*
Ditylenchus Sturhan & Friedman, 1965 *1120*

A—*convallariae*, *Pratylenchus*
Add: *993* syn: *Pratylenchus pratensis* of Slootweg, 1956

A—*coprophages*, *Diplogaster*
1. Place asterisk before *Paroigolaimella*
2. Add: *valid name according to Meyl, 1961 *1028*

PAGE 32

N—*coprophagus*, var. *longicaudatus*
Rhabditoides Kannan, 1960 *955*

A—*corii*, *Dorylaimus*
Add: NOTE: placed in *species inquirendae* by Meyl, 1961 *1028*

A—*cornelli*, *Tylencholaimus*
Add: *Doryllium* (van der Linde, 1938) Jairajpuri & Siddiqi, 1963 *946*

N—*corniformis*
Chiloplacus Erzhanov, 1964 *852a*

A—*cornis*, *Acrobeles*
Add: *Cephalobus* [*Cephalobus*] (*c*)

crassianulatum

(Thorne, 1925) Thorne, 1937 *786*
Chiloplacus (Thorne, 1925) Goodey, 1963 *881*

N—*cornus*
Plectus Maggenti, 1961 *1020*
Proteroplectus (Maggenti, 1961) Paramonov, 1964 *1040*

C,T—*coronata*, *Rhabditis*
1. Change species name to *coronatus*
2. Transpose entire entry to immediately after *coronatus*, *Plectonchus*

N—*coronatum*
Doryllium Brzeski, 1962 *790*

N—*coronatus*
Basirotyleptus Siddiqi & Khan, 1965 *1109*

A—*coronatus*, *Hoplolaimus*
Add: *1065* = *Nemonchus galeatus* Cobb, 1913

N—*coronatus*
Paratylenchus Colbran, 1965 *832d*

A—*costatus*, *Actinolaimus*
Add: *Actinca* (Schneider, 1936) Andrássy, 1964 *781*

PAGE 33

A—*costatus*, *Tylenchus*
1. Place asterisk before *Tylenchus* [*Aglenchus*]
2. Add: *Aglenchus* (de Man, 1921) Meyl, 1961 *1028*
*valid name according to Goodey, 1963 *881*

N—*cottieri*
Trichodorus Clark, 1963 *824*

N—*coxi*
Xiphinema Tarjan, 1964 *1126*

A—*crassa*, *Monhystera*
Add: NOTE: placed in *species inquirendae* by Meyl, 1961 *1028*

N—*crassianulatum*
Criconemoides de Guiran, 1963 *892* (*c*)

17

crassicauda

889 syn: *Criconemoides deconincki* de Grisse, 1963
Lobocriconema (de Guiran, 1963) de Grisse & Loof, 1965 *891*

A—*crassicauda, Tripyla*
Add: NOTE: (2) placed in *species inquirendae* by Brzeski, 1964 *806*

N—*crassicaudatus*
Tylenchorhynchus Williams, 1960 *1147*

A,C—*crassoides, Dorylaimus*
1. Delete asterisks and footnote
2. Add: *Mesodorylaimus* (Jägerskiöld, 1908) Goodey, 1963 *881*

A,C—*crassus, Dorylaimus*
1. Delete asterisks and footnote
2. Add: *994* syn: *Dorylaimus robustus* of de Man, 1884 (male, in part)
995 syn: *Dorylaimus stagnalis fecundus*, var. *pseudocrassus* Micoletzky, 1925
Mesodorylaimus (de Man, 1884) Goodey, 1963 *881*
NOTE: *Dorylaimus crassus* of Micoletzky, 1925 is regarded as *species inquirenda* by Loof, 1961 *995*

N—*crenata*
Criconemoides Loof, 1964 *1000*
Macroposthonia (Loof, 1964) de Grisse & Loof, 1965 *891*
Neocriconema (Loof, 1964) Diab & Jenkins, 1965 *845*
Mesocriconema (Loof, 1964) Andrássy, 1965 *781b*

A—*crenati, Aphelenchoides*
Add: *Bursaphelenchus* (Rühm, 1956) Goodey, 1960 *876*

A—*crenati, Parasitorhabditis*
Add: NOTE: (2) placed in *species inquirendae* by Goodey, 1963 *881*

N—*crenatus*
Helicotylenchus Das, 1960 *842*

N—*crenatus*
Pratylenchus Loof, 1960 *993* (*c*)

curvidentata

993 syn: *Anguillulina pratensis* of Goffart, 1929 in part
993 syn: *Pratylenchus pratensis* of Thorne, 1949; Sher & Allen, 1953; Oostenbrink, 1954; and Coomans, 1958 in part

PAGE 34

A—*cristatus, Mononchus*
Add: NOTE: (2) placed in *species inquirendae* by Clark, 1960 *815*

N—*croca*
Santafea Massey, 1963 *1025*

A,C—*crotaloides, Iota*
1. Delete asterisks and footnote
2. Add: *Nothocriconema* (Cobb, 1924) de Grisse & Loof, 1965 *891*

A—*cruznema, Cruznema*
1. Place asterisk before *Cruznema*
2. Add: *regarded a valid species by Thorne, 1961 *1132*

A—*cryphali, Parasitaphelenchus*
Add: *Bursaphelenchus* (Fuchs, 1930) Goodey, 1960 *876*

PAGE 35

A—*cunicularii, Ektaphelenchus*
Add: *876* = *Aphelenchus hylastophilus* (Fuchs, 1930) Filipjev, 1934

N—*curiosus*
Tetylenchus Wilski, 1964 *1152*

A,C—*curvatum, Criconemoides*
1. Change species name to *curvata*
2. Add: *Macroposthonia* (Raski, 1952) de Grisse & Loof, 1965 *891*

N—*curvatus*
Dorylaimellus Jairajpuri, 1964 *936*

N—*curvatus*
Helicotylenchus Román, 1965 *1052*

A—*curvidentata, Diplogaster*
Add: NOTE: placed in *species inquirendae* by Meyl, 1961 *1028*

curvidentis

A—curvidentis, Parasitaphelenchus
Add: NOTE: placed in species inquirendae by Goodey, 1960 876

A,C—curvitata, Paratylenchus
1. Change species name to curvitatus
2. Add: 1124 syn: Paratylenchus dianthus Jenkins & Taylor, 1956

N—curvus
Tylenchorhynchus Williams, 1960 1147

A—curzii, Cylindrogaster
Add: 881 syn: Cylindrocorpus curzii
zamithi Lordello, 1953

A—curzii zamithi, Cylindrogaster
Add: 881 = Cylindrogaster curzii
Goodey, 1935

N—cuspidatus
Eudorylaimus Andrássy, 1964 778

N—cylindrica
Belondira Thorne, 1964 1133

N—cylindrica
Phellonema Thorne, 1964 1133

A—cylindricaudatum, Xiphinema
Add: NOTE: placed in species inquirendae by Sturhan, 1963 1119

A—cylindricaudatus, Tylenchus
1. Place asterisk before Aphelenchus
2. Add: 876 = Aphelenchus avenae
Bastian, 1865
*valid genus according to Para-
monov, 1964 1040

A—cylindricum, Criconema
1. Add: 891 = Iota simile Cobb, 1918

PAGE 36

A—cylindricum, Triplonchium
Add: Tylolaimophorus (Cobb, 1920)
Goodey, 1963 881

A—cylindricus, Bathyodontus
Add: 925 syn: Mirolaimus mirus Andrássy, 1956

N—cylindricus
Trichodorus Hooper, 1962 910

dahli

C—cylindricus, Tylenchorhynchus
In ninth line under species name
change Tylenchus to Tylenchorhynchus

N—cyperi
Heterodera Golden, Rau & Cobb, 1962
874

N—dacchensis
Diplogaster [Diplogaster] Timm, 1961
1136
Diplogastrellus (Timm, 1961) Timm,
1961 1136

N—dactylurus
Dorylaimoides Heyns, 1963 904

N—dactylurus
Tylenchorhynchus Das, 1960 842

A—dadayi, Dorylaimus
Add: Mesodorylaimus (Thorne &
Swanger, 1936) Goodey, 1963 881

N—dadayi
Monhystera Goodey, 1963 881
881 syn: Prismatolaimus macrurus
Daday, 1899

A—dadayi, Mononchus
1. Place asterisk before 478 on line 4
under species name
2. Add: Iotonchus (Micoletzky, 1914)
Altherr, 1960 753
Miconchus (Micoletzky, 1914)
Mulvey, 1962 1032
753 syn: Mononchus [Iotonchus]
rapax Cobb, 1917
*invalid synonymy according to
Mulvey, 1962 1032
NOTE: placed in species inquirendae
by Clark, 1960 815

A—dadayi, Prismatolaimus
Add: NOTE: questionably regarded as
species inquirenda by Andrássy,
1964, 780

N—dahli
Dorylaimus Altherr, 1960 753
Prodorylaimus (Altherr, 1960) An-
drássy, 1964 781

19

N—danubialis
Nothotylenchus Andrássy, 1960 763

N—daoi
Chronogaster Loof, 1964 1001

A—darbouxi, Tylenchus
Add: NOTE: placed in species inquirendae by Meyl, 1961 1028

A,C—davainei, Tylenchus
1. Delete asterisks and footnote
2. Place asterisk before Tylenchus
[Tylenchus]
3. Add: *valid name according to
Goodey, 1963 881

A—davainei tenuis, Tylenchus
Add: 1028 = Tylenchus kischkei Meyl,
1961
881 = Tylenchus [Tylenchus] tenuis
Kischke, 1956

PAGE 37

A—debilicauda, Rhabditis
Add: NOTE: placed in species inquirendae by Meyl, 1961 1028

A,C—declinatoaculeatus, Dorylaimus
1. Delete asterisks and footnote
2. Add: Drepanodorus (Kreis, 1924)
Brzeski, 1964 805

N—deconincki
Chiloplacus Coomans, 1962 835

N—deconincki
Criconemoides de Grisse, 1963 885
889 = Criconemoides crassianulatum
de Guiran, 1963

N—deletrix
Micronema Anderson & Bemrick, 1965
759

N—delicatus
Mesodorylaimus Lordello, 1965 1004a

A,C—demani, Aphelenchus
1. Delete asterisks and footnote
2. Add: Seinura (Goodey, 1928)
Goodey, 1960 876

A—demani, Criconema
Add: Nothocriconema (Micoletzky,
1925) de Grisse & Loof, 1965 891

A—demani, Diplogaster
Add: Diplogasteriana (Schneider,
1923) Goodey, 1963 881
NOTE: placed in species inquirendae
by Meyl, 1961 1028

N—demani
Dorylaimellus Goodey, 1963 881
881 syn: Tylencholaimus mirabilis of
de Man, 1876, 1880 & 1884
881 syn: Dorylaimellus mirabilis of
Goodey, 1951
NOTE: Heyns, 1963 906 recognizes
J. B. Goodey, 1963 881 as renam-
ing Dorylaimellus mirabilis of
T. Goodey, 1951 293 as D. demani.
In Heyns' German summary, however, he then proposes that D.
mirabilis of T. Goodey, 1951 be re-
named D. goodeyi. Obviously, D.
demani is the valid name since it
predates D. goodeyi.

A—demani, Monhystera
Add: NOTE: placed in species inquirendae by Meyl, 1961 1028

A—demani, Plectus
Add: NOTE: placed in species inquirendae by Meyl, 1961 1028

N—demani
Sectonema Altherr, 1965 757a
757a syn: ? Dorylaimus robustus of
de Man, 1921

A—dendrophilus, Diplogaster
Add: Diplogastrellus (Weingärtner in
Körner, 1954) Meyl, 1961 1028
Diplogasteritus (Weingärtner in
Körner, 1954) Goodey, 1963 881

PAGE 38

A—dendrophilus, Tylenchus
Add: Neoditylenchus (Marcinowski,
1909) Meyl, 1961 1028

A—dentata, Bunonema
Add: Serronema (Paesler, 1957)
Goodey, 1963 881

A—*dentata, Tripyla*
Add: NOTE: placed in *species inquirendae* by Meyl, 1961 *1028*

A—*denticulatus, Mononchus*
Add: NOTE: placed in *species inquirendae* by Mulvey, 1961 *1030*

A—*desertus, Acrobeles*
Add: *Cervidellus* (Kirjanova, 1951) Goodey, 1963 *881*

A—*desidiosus, Acrobeles*
Add: *Cervidellus* (Kirjanova, 1951) Meyl, 1961 *1028*

A—*detritophagus, Panagrolaimus*
Add: *881 Panagrolaimus detritophagus* of Rühm, 1956 = *Panagrolaimus paradetritophagus* Goodey, 1963

A—*deuberti, Dorylaimus*
Add: *Mesodorylaimus* (Andrássy, 1958) Goodey, 1963 *881*

PAGE 39

N—*devimucronatus*
Cervidellus Sumenkova, 1964 *1121a*

N—*dianae*
Cobbonchus Coetzee, 1965 *829*

A—*dianthus, Paratylenchus*
Add: *1124 = Paratylenchus curvitatus* van der Linde, 1938

N—*dibulbosum*
Altherrnema Brzeski, 1961 *787a*
806a = Rhabditis schneideri Bütschli, 1873

A—*didentatus, Diplogaster*
Add: NOTE: placed in *species inquirendae* by Goodey, 1963 *881*

A,C—*digicaudatum, Xiphinema*
1. Change species name to *digiticaudatum*
2. Add: NOTE: placed in *species inquirendae* by Luc & Tarjan, 1963 *1019*

N—*digitatus*
Dorylaimellus Siddiqi, 1964 *1092a*

N—*digitatus*
Helicotylenchus Siddiqi & Husain, 1964 *1105*

N—*digitatus*
Tylenchorhynchus Das, 1960 *842*

N—*digitulus*
Bursaphelenchus Loof, 1964 *1001*

A—*dihystera, Tylenchus*
Add: *Helicotylenchus* (Cobb, 1893) Sher, 1961 *1065*
1065 syn: *Tylenchus olaae* Cobb, 1906
1065 syn: *Aphelenchus dubius*, var. *peruensis* Steiner, 1920
1065 syn: *Tylenchus spiralis* Cassidy, 1930
1065 syn: *Helicotylenchus nannus* Steiner, 1945

A,C—*dimidius, Tetylenchus*
1. Change Loof, 1959 to Loof, 1960
2. Add: NOTE: regarded as valid species by Goodey, 1963 *881* but not by Merny, 1964 *1027*

A—*dintheriana, Monhystera*
Add: NOTE: placed in *species inquirendae* by Meyl, 1961 *1028*

A—*dioscoreae, Scutellonema*
Add: *1067 = Hoplolaimus bradys* Steiner & LeHew, 1933

A—*dipapillatus, Hexatylus*
Add: *1028 = Hexatylus viviparus* Goodey, 1926

A,C—*diplogaster, Allantonema*
1. Delete lines 12 and 13 (on page 40) under the species name
2. Place asterisk before *Diplogaster*
3. Add: *this taxon considered *species inquirenda* by Meyl, 1961 *1028*

PAGE 40

A—*dipsaci, Anguillula*
Add: *881* syn: *Anguillulina dipsaci*, var. *allocutus* Steiner, 1934
881 syn: *Ditylenchus allocutus* Filipjev & Schuurmans Stekhoven, 1941 (*c*)

dipsaci

881 syn: *Anguillulina dipsaci,* var. *amsinckiae* Steiner & Scott, 1935
881 syn: *Ditylenchus amsinckiae* Filipjev & Schuurmans Stekhoven, 1941
881 syn: *Tylenchus dipsaci,* var. *tobaensis* Schneider, 1937
881 syn: *Ditylenchus tobaensis* Kirjanova, 1951
881 syn: *Ditylenchus dipsaci,* var. *narcissi* Filipjev & Schuurmans Stekhoven, 1941
881 syn: *Ditylenchus dipsaci,* var. *hyacinthi* (Prillieux, 1881) Filipjev & Schuurmans Stekhoven, 1941
881 syn: *Ditylenchus phloxidis* Kirjanova, 1951

A—dipsaci, var. *allocutus, Anguillulina*
Add: *881* = *Anguillula dipsaci* Kühn, 1857

A—dipsaci, var. *amsinckiae, Anguillulina*
Add: *881* = *Anguillula dipsaci* Kuhn,

A—dipsaci, var. *hyacinthi, Ditylenchus*
Add: (Prillieux, 1881) in first line under species name, directly after *Ditylenchus*
881 = *Anguillula dipsaci* Kühn, 1857

A—dipsaci, var. *narcissi, Ditylenchus*
Add: *881* = *Anguillula dipsaci* Kühn, 1857

A—dipsaci, var. *tobaensis, Tylenchus*
Add: *881* = *Anguillula dipsaci* Kühn, 1857

N—directus
Dorylaimellus Heyns, 1964 *906*

PAGE 41

N—discocephalus
Dorylaimellus Siddiqi, 1964 *1089*

A—discrepans, Tylenchus
1. Place asterisk before *Tylenchus*
2. Add: *Lelenchus* (Andrássy, 1954) Meyl, 1961 *1028*
   *valid name according to Goodey, 1963 *881*

dolichurus

PAGE 42

A—distinctus, Acrobeles
Add: *Cervidellus* (Kirjanova, 1951) Goodey, 1963 *881*

N—ditissimus
Tylenchus Brzeski, 1963 *804*

A—ditlevseni, Bunonema
1. Place asterisk before *Bunonema*
2. Add: *valid name according to Goodey, 1963 *881*

A—diversicaudatum, Dorylaimus
Add: *1019* syn: *Xiphinema paraelongatum* Altherr, 1958

A—diversipapillatus, Cephalobus
Add: *Eucephalobus* (Daday, 1905) Goodey, 1963 *881*
NOTE: may be a synonym of *Cephalobus striatus* Bastian, 1865 according to Goodey, 1963 *881*

A,C—diversipapillatus, Trilobus
1. Delete asterisks and footnote
2. Place asterisk before *631*
3. Add: *valid synonymy according to Andrássy, 1964 *777*

A,C—diversus, Aphelenchoides
1. Change species name to *diversa*
2. Transpose entire entry to immediately after *ditlevseni, Dorylaimus*
3. Add: *Seinura* (Paesler, 1957) Goodey, 1960 *876*

N—divittatus
Tylenchorhynchus Siddiqi, 1961 *1078*

PAGE 43

A,C—dolichurus, Monhystera
1. Delete asterisks and footnote
2. Add: NOTE: placed in *species inquirendae* by Meyl, 1961 *1028*, but regarded a valid species by Andrássy, 1961 *766*

A—dolichurus, Prismatolaimus
1. Place asterisks before second and third entry below species name
2. Add: *780* syn: *Prismatolaimus doli-* (*c*)

22

churus, f. *minimus* Micoletzky, 1922
* invalid synonymies according to Milne, 1963 *1029*

A—*dolichurus*, var. *brevicaudatus*, *Prismatolaimus*
Add: *761* = *Prismatolaimus brevicaudatus* Andrássy, 1960

A—*dolichurus*, var. *bulbosus*, *Prismatolaimus*
Add: *1029* = *Prismatolaimus bulbosus* Milne, 1963

A—*dolichurus*, f. *minimus*, *Prismatolaimus*
Add: *780* = *Prismatolaimus dolichurus* de Man, 1880

N—*dorae*
Tylencholaimus Kruger, 1965 *989*

A—*dorsobidentata*, *Anguillulina*
Add: *Panagrellus* (Rühm, 1956) Baker, 1962 *784*

N—*drepanodon*
Carcharolaimus Loof, 1964 *1001*

A—*dreyeri*, *Dorylaimus*
Add: *Mesodorylaimus* (van der Linde, 1938) Goodey, 1963 *881*

PAGE 44

C—*dryocoeti*, *Diplogaster*
Delete entire entry; it is *nomen nudum*

A—*dryocoeti*, *Fuchsia*
Add: *Mikoletzkya* (Rühm, 1956) Baker, 1962 *784*

A—*dryophilus*, *Trilobus*
Add: NOTE: placed in *species inquirendae* by Meyl, 1961 *1028*

A,C—*dubius*, *Cephalobus*
1. Delete asterisks and footnote
2. Add: *Cephalobus* [*Cephalobus*] Maupas, 1900 *786*

A—*dubius*, *Diplogaster*
Add: NOTE: placed in *species inquirendae* by Goodey, 1963 *881*

A—*dubius*, *Monhystera*
Add: NOTE: placed in *species inquirendae* by Meyl, 1961 *1028*

N—*dubius*
Panagrellus Sanwal, 1960 *1058*

A—*dubius*, *Parasitaphelenchus*
Add: NOTE: placed in *species inquirendae* by Goodey, 1960 *876*

PAGE 45

A—*dubius*, var. *apicata*, *Cephalobus*
Add: = between *484* and *Cephalobus*

A—*dubius*, var. *peruensis*, *Aphelenchus*
Add: *1065* = *Tylenchus dihystera* Cobb, 1893

N—*duhouxi*
Eudorylaimus Altherr, 1963 *755*

A—*duplexus*, *Psilenchus*
1. Place asterisk before *Tylenchus*
2. Add: *Filenchus* (Hagemeyer & Allen, 1952) Baker, 1962 *784*
* valid genus according to Goodey, 1963 *881*

N—*duplicivestitum*
Criconemoides Andrássy, 1963 *774*
Nothocriconema (Andrássy, 1963) de Grisse & Loof, 1965 *891*

N—*duplopapillata*
Vanderlindia Heyns, 1964 *907*

N—*ebriensis*
Tylenchorhynchus Seinhorst, 1963 *1064*

A—*effilatum*, *Xiphinema*
Add: NOTE: placed in *species inquirendae* by Luc & Tarjan, 1963 *1019*

A—*effilatus*, *Plectus*
Add: NOTE: placed in *species inquirendae* by Moyl, 1961 *1028*

A—*eggersi*, *Aphelenchoides*
Add: *Bursaphelenchus* (Rühm, 1956) Goodey, 1960 *876*

N—*egyptiensis*
Helicotylenchus Tarjan, 1964 *1127*

eidmanni

A—*eidmanni, Aphelenchoides*
Add: *Bursaphelenchus* (Rühm, 1956)
Goodey, 1960 *876*

PAGE 46

N—*elaboratus*
Dorylaimoides Siddiqi, 1965 *1096*

A—*elachistus, Paratylenchus*
Add: *1124* syn: *Paratylenchus minutus* Linford in Linford, Oliveira, & Ishii, 1949

N—*elegans*
Axonchium Jairajpuri, 1964 *936*

A—*elegans, Craspedonema*
Add: *Bunonema* (Rahm, 1928) Baker, 1962 *784*
NOTE: placed in *species inquirendae* by Goodey, 1963 *881*

A—*elegans, Diplogaster*
Add: *Mononchoides* (Weingärtner, 1955) Goodey, 1963 *881*

N—*elegans*
Gracilacus Raski, 1962 *1044*
Paratylenchus (Raski, 1962) Siddiqi & Goodey, 1964 *1103*

N—*elegans*
Helicotylenchus Román, 1965 *1052*

C—*elegans, Rhabditis*
On first line change 1900 *445* to 1899 *444*

N—*elegans*
Tylenchorhynchus Siddiqi, 1961 *1078*

A—*elegans, Tylenchus*
Add: *995* = *Tylenchus davainei* Bastian, 1865
NOTE: placed in *species inquirendae* by Meyl, 1961 *1028*

A—*elegans,* var. *paulistanum, Craspedonema*
Add: NOTE: placed in *species inquirendae* by Goodey, 1963 *881*

elymi

A—*elegans,* f. *bryophilus, Alaimus*
Add: *766* = *Alaimus bryophilus* Andrássy, 1961

A—*elegantula, Criconema*
Add: *Criconemoides* (Gunhold, 1953) Oostenbrink, 1960
891 = *Criconema longulum* Gunhold, 1953

A—*elisensis, Rotylenchus*
Add: *Helicotylenchus* (Carvalho, 1957) Carvalho, 1959 *811*
1065 = *Rotylenchulus reniformis* Linford & Oliveira, 1940

A—*elmiraensis, Aphelenchoides*
Add: *Seinura* (van der Linde, 1938) Goodey, 1960 *876*

PAGE 47

A—*elongatum, Xiphinema*
Add: *1019* syn: *Xiphinema pratense* Loos, 1949
1019 syn: *Xiphinema campinense* Lordello, 1951

A—*elongatus, Aphelenchoides*
Add: NOTE: placed in *species inquirendae* by Goodey, 1960 *876*

A—*elongatus, Dorylaimus*
Add: *1080* syn: *Longidorus menthasolanus* Konicek & Jensen, 1961
1118 syn: *Longidorus monohystera* Altherr, 1953
909 Longidorus elongatus of Goodey, 1951 = *Longidorus goodeyi* Hooper, 1961

N—*elongatus*
Oxydirus Altherr, 1963 *755*

N—*elongatus*
Plectus Maggenti, 1961 *1020*
Proteroplectus (Maggenti, 1961) Paramonov, 1964 *1040*

A—*elymi, Plectus*
Add: NOTE: (2) regarded *nomen dubium* by Maggenti, 1961 *1020*

24

A—*emarginatus, Tylenchus*
1. Place asterisk before *Tylenchus*
2. Add: *832a* syn: *Tylenchus hexalineatus* Geraert, 1962
   832a syn: *Tylenchus [Cephalenchus] megacephalus* Goodey, 1962
   *valid name according to Colbran, 1964 *832a*

A—*engadinensis, Dorylaimus*
Add: *Dorylaimellus* (Altherr, 1950) Jairajpuri, 1964 *936*

N—*ensicaudatus*
Acrobeles Thomas & Allen, 1965 *1131*

A—*epacris, Cacopaurus*
Add: *Gracilacus* (Allen & Jensen, 1950) Raski, 1962 *1044*
Paratylenchus (Allen & Jensen, 1950) Goodey, 1963 *881*

N—*equalis*
Ditylenchus Heyns, 1964 *905*

N—*erdelyii*
Mesodorylaimus Andrássy, 1965 *781a*

N—*eremitus*
Aphelenchus Thorne, 1961 *1132*

A—*eremus, Aphelenchoides*
Add: *Bursaphelenchus* (Rühm, 1956) Goodey, 1960 *876*

PAGE 48

A—*eremus, Ditylenchus*
Add: *Neoditylenchus* (Rühm, 1956) Meyl, 1961 *1028*

A—*erlangensis, Diplogaster*
1. Place asterisk before *Allodiplogaster*
2. Add: *valid genus according to Meyl, 1961 *1028*

A—*erraticus, Aphelenchus*
Add: NOTE: placed in *species inquirendae* by Goodey, 1960 *876*

N—*erriae*
Paralongidorus Heyns, 1965 *908a*

N—*eskei*
Tylencholaimellus Siddiqi & Khan, 1964 *1107*

A—*esseri, Xiphinemella*
Add: *Botalium* (Chitwood, 1957) Heyns, 1963 *903*

N—*estonica*
Heterodera Kirjanova & Krall, 1963 *985*

N—*eucalypti*
Paralongidorus Fisher, 1964 *856*

A—*eucarpus, Aphelenchoides*
Add: *Bursaphelenchus* (Rühm, 1956) Goodey, 1960 *876*

N—*eudorylaimoides*
Labronema Geraert, 1962 *865*

N—*eugeniae*
Hemicycliophora Khan & Basir, 1963 *964*

A—*eurycephalus, Diplogaster*
Add: *Anchidiplogaster* (Völk, 1950) Meyl, 1961 *1028*
Diplogasteritus (Völk, 1950) Goodey, 1963 *881*

A—*eurycephalus, Tylenchus*
Add: NOTE: (2) placed in *species inquirendae* by Meyl, 1961 *1028*

N—*eurycerus*
Plectus Massey, 1964 *1025a*

N—*eurysoma*
Criconema Golden & Friedman, 1964 *873*

N—*eurystoma*
Cobbonchus Coetzee, 1965 *829*

A—*eutelesa, Fuchsia*
Add: *Mikoletzkya* (Rühm, 1956) Baker, 1962 *784*

C—*eutelesus, Diplogaster*
Delete entire entry since it is *nomen nudum*

N—*euthychilus*
Belonolaimus Rau, 1963 *1046*

N—*eversum*
Botalium Heyns, 1963 *903*

PAGE 49

A—*exiguus, Tylenchus*
Add: NOTE: placed in *species inquirendae* by Loof, 1961 *995*, but regarded as valid species by Thorne, 1961 *1132*

N—*exilis*
Amphidelus Andrássy, 1962 *769*

N—*eximius*
Rotylenchus Siddiqi, 1964 *1092*

N—*eximius*
Trichonchium Siddiqi & Khan, 1964 *1110*
Basirotyleptus (Siddiqi & Khan, 1964) Siddiqi & Khan, 1965 *1109*

A—*extricatus, Epimenides*
Add: *881* = *Rhabditis lambdiensis* Maupas, 1919

A—*faecalis, Diplogaster*
Add: *Holodiplogaster* (Weingärtner in Meyl, 1956) Meyl, 1961 *1028*
Fictor (Weingärtner in Meyl, 1956) Goodey, 1963 *881*

C—*falciformis, Trichotylenchus*
Change 1959 to 1960

N—*fallorobustus*
Rotylenchus Sher, 1965 *1071*
1071 syn: *Anguillulina robusta* of Goodey, 1932 in part, *Rotylenchus robustus* of Filipjev and Schuurmans Stekhoven, 1941 in part, and of Goodey and Seinhorst, 1960

PAGE 50

A—*fecundus, Dorylaimus*
Add: *Mesodorylaimus* (Cobb, 1914) Goodey, 1963 *881*

C,T—*felox, Theristus*
1. Change species name to *velox*
2. Transfer entire entry to immediately after *velox, Plectus* on page 155

C—*femina, Hoplotylus*
Change 1959 to 1960

A—*ferniae, Criconemoides*
Add: *Macroposthonia* (Luc, 1959) de Grisse & Loof, 1965 *891*
891 syn: *Criconemoides obtusicaudatum* Heyns, 1962

A—*ferrandini, Aphelenchoides*
Add: NOTE: (1) placed in *species inquirendae* by Goodey, 1960 *876*
(2) regarded a valid species by Meyl, 1961 *1028*

A—*festivus, Dorylaimus*
Add: NOTE: placed in *species inquirendae* by Meyl, 1961 *1028*

A—*fici, Heterodera*
1. Place asterisk before *Heterodera*
2. Add: *valid name according to Meyl, 1961 *1028*

A—*fictor, Diplogaster*
Add: *Eudiplogaster* (Bastian, 1865) Meyl, 1961 *1028*
Mononchoides (Bastian, 1865) Goodey, 1963 *881*

N—*filiarum*
Prodorylaimus Andrássy, 1964 *779*

A—*filicaudata, Macfadyenia*
Add: NOTE: placed in *species inquirendae* by Goodey, 1963 *881*

N—*filicaudata*
Seinura Goodey, 1960 *876*
876 syn: *Aphelenchoides winchesi,* var. *filicaudatus* Christie, 1939

A—*filicaudata, Tripyla*
Add: *995* syn: *Tripyla filicaudata,* var. *austriaca* Micoletzky, 1922
806 syn: *Tripyla filicaudata,* var. *hoehnei* Rahm, 1928

A—*filicaudata,* var. *austriaca, Tripyla*
Add: *995* = *Tripyla filicaudata* de Man, 1880
NOTE: placed in *varietas inquirendum* by Brzeski, 1964 *806*

A—*filicaudata,* var. *hoehnei, Tripyla*
Add: *806* = *Tripyla filicaudata* de Man, 1880
NOTE: placed in *species inquirendae* by Loof, 1961 *995*

filicaudatum

A—filicaudatum, Glauxinema
Add: NOTE: placed in species inquirendae by Goodey, 1963 881

A—filicaudatus, Butlerius
1. Place asterisk before Butlerius
2. Add: Butleriellus (Adam, 1930) Meyl, 1961 1028
*valid genus according to Goodey, 1963 881

PAGE 51

A—filicaudatus, Diplogaster
Add: NOTE: placed in species inquirendae by Meyl, 1961 1028

N—filicaudatus
Dorylaimellus Thorne, 1964 1133

A,C—filicaudatus, Dorylaimus
1. Delete asterisks and footnote
2. Add: Mesodorylaimus (Daday, 1905) Goodey, 1963 881

N—filiforme
Thornenema Siddiqi, 1965 1098a

A—filiformis, Diplogaster
Add: NOTE: placed in species inquirendae by Meyl, 1961 1028

N—filiformis
Dorylaimellus Jairajpuri, 1964 936

A—filiformis, Dorylaimus
Add: Mesodorylaimus (Bastian, 1865) Goodey, 1963 881
781 Dorylaimus filiformis of Allgén, 1952 in part = Dorylaimus loeffleri Andrássy, 1964

A,C—filiformis, Tylenchus
1. Delete footnote
2. Add: Filenchus (Bütschli, 1873) Meyl, 1961 1028
801 Tylenchus filiformis of Andrássy, 1954 = Tylenchus vulgaris Brzeski, 1963
*valid name according to Brzeski, 1963 801
NOTE: Tylenchus filiformis of de Man, 1876 placed in species inquirendae by Loof, 1961 995

flevensis

A—filiformis, var. fukiensis, Monhystera
Add: NOTE: regarded a dubious species by Andrássy, 1960 761

PAGE 52

A—filiformis, var. longicaudata, Monhystera
Add: NOTE: placed in species inquirendae by Meyl, 1961 1028

A—filiformis, var. salina, Monhystera
Add: 1028 = Monhystera salina Meyl, 1961

A—filipjevi, Promononchus
Add: 806 = Tripyla glomerans Bastian, 1865

PAGE 53

N—flagellatus
Tobrilus Andrássy, 1963 774

A—flagellicauda, Rhabdititoides
Add: NOTE: placed in species inquirendae by Goodey, 1963 881

N—flagellicaudatum
Xiphinema Luc, 1961 1010

N—flagellicaudatus
Eudiplogaster Andrássy, 1962 769a

A—flagellicaudatus, Pararhabditis
Add: Neorhabditis (Schuurmans Stekhoven, 1951) Baker, 1962 784

N—flandriensis
Criconemoides de Grisse, 1964 887
891 = Hoplolaimus informe Micoletzky, 1922

N—flangum
Doryllium Thorne, 1964 1133

N—flatus
Helicotylenchus Román, 1965 1052

A—flavomaculatus, Dorylaimus
Add: Mesodorylaimus (Linstow, 1876) Goodey, 1963 881

N—flevensis
Trichodorus Kuiper & Loof, 1962 990
912 = Trichodorus teres Hooper, 1962

27

flexus

A—flexus, Dorylaimus
Add: Mesodorylaimus (Thorne & Swanger, 1936) Goodey, 1963 881

A—floridensis, Hemicriconemoides
Add: Hemicycliophora (Chitwood & Birchfield, 1957) Goodey, 1963 881

A—floridensis, Trophotylenchulus
Add: Tylenchulus (Raski, 1957) Maggenti, 1962 1021

A—florisbella, Demaniella
Add: NOTE: placed in species inquirendae by Timm, 1963 1138

N—fluviatilis
Aphelenchoides Andrássy, 1960 763

A—fluviatilis, Rhabditis
Add: 922 = Rhabditis marina Bastian, 1865

A,C—foetidus, Aphelenchus
1. Delete asterisks and footnote
2. Delete second and third lines under species name
3. Add: †Tylopharynx (Bütschli, 1874) Goffart, 1930 244
   881 syn: Tylopharynx striata de Man, 1876

PAGE 54

A—fortidens, Diplogaster
Add: NOTE: placed in species inquirendae by Goodey, 1963 881

A,C—fragariae, Aphelenchus
1. In first line under species name change 449a to 549a
2. Place asterisk before Aphelenchoides on line 10
3. Add: *valid name according to Sanwal, 1961 1060

N—fransus
Eudorylaimus Heyns, 1963 904

A—franzi, Tricephalobus
Add: Trilabiatus (Rühm, 1956) Goodey, 1963 881

A—fraudulentus, Aphelenchoides
Add: Bursaphelenchus (Rühm, 1956) Goodey, 1960 876

galeatus

A—frigophilus, Plectus
Add: NOTE: regarded as nomen dubium by Maggenti, 1961 1020

A—frugicola, Brevibucca
Add: Rhabditoides (Goodey, 1942) Goodey, 1963 881

N—fruticicolae
Rhabditis Shinohara, 1960 1072

PAGE 55

N—fungivorus
Bursaphelenchus Franklin & Hooper, 1962 862

A—fuorni, Dorylaimus
Add: Pungentus (Altherr, 1950) Goodey, 1963 881
Dorylaimellus (Altherr, 1950) Jairajpuri, 1964 936
NOTE: placed in species inquirendae by Meyl, 1961 1028

N—fuscilabiatus
Onchulus Altherr, 1965 757a

A,C—fusiformis, Plectus
1. Add: 1020 = Plectus parietinus Bastian, 1865
2. Change NOTE to: placed in species inquirendae by Meyl, 1961 1028

A—gaddi, Criconemoides
1. Place asterisk before Hemicriconemoides
2. Add: Hemicycliophora (Loos, 1949) Goodey, 1963 881
   *valid genus according to Siddiqi & Goodey, 1964 1103

N—gadeai
Pratylenchoides Arias Delgado, Jiménez Millán, & López Pedregal, 1965 782

A—galeatus, Nemonchus
Add: †Hoplolaimus (Cobb, 1913) Filipjev & Schuurmans Stekhoven, 1941 212
   1065 syn: Hoplolaimus coronatus Cobb, 1923

galeopsidis

A—*galeopsidis, Heterodera*
1. Place asterisk before *Heterodera* on line 1
2. Add: *valid name according to Goodey, 1963 *881*

A—*gallagheri, Aphelenchoides*
Add: *Parasitaphelenchus* (Massey, 1960) Goodey, 1960 *876*

A—*gallicus, Anguillulina*
Add: *Neoditylenchus* (Steiner, 1935) Meyl, 1961 *1028*

N—*gallicus*
Mesotylus de Guiran, 1964 *894*
1129 = Pratylenchoides guevarai Tobar Jiménez, 1963

A—*gaussi, Dorylaimus*
Add: *Mesodorylaimus* (Steiner, 1916) Goodey, 1963 *881*

N—*geminus*
Iotonchus Heyns & Lagerwey, 1965 *908c*

N—*geniculatus*
Eudorylaimus Andrássy, 1961 *766a*
Afrodorylaimus (Andrássy, 1961) Andrássy, 1964 *781*

C—*geophila, Spilophora*
Change lines four and five to *Dichromadora* (de Man, 1876) Kreis, 1929 *355*

A,C—*geophilus, Plectus*
1. Delete asterisks and footnote
2. Add: NOTE: placed in *species inquirendae* by Maggenti, 1961 *1020*

A—*georgiensis, Criconema*
Add: NOTE: (1) Hopper, 1963 *914a* regards the male of this species as *incertae sedis*.
(2) Siddiqi & Goodey, 1964 *1103* erroneously regarded this species as *nomen nudum*, apparently overlooking the figure that was given.

A—*georgiensis, Longidorus*
Add: NOTE: Siddiqi, 1965 *1097* felt that this species should be transferred to *Paralongidorus*.

glomerans

N—*georgii*
Criconemoides Prasad, Khan & Mathur, 1965 *1043b*

PAGE 56

N—*gertii*
Tylencholaimus Kruger, 1965 *989*

N—*ghanae*
Mesodorylaimus Andrássy, 1965 *781a*

A—*gibberoaculeatus, Dorylaimus*
Add: *Eudorylaimus* (Kreis, 1930) Andrássy, 1960 *761*

A—*gigantea, Tripyla*
Add: NOTE: (2) placed in *species inquirendae* by Brzeski, 1964 *806*

A—*gigas, Radopholus*
Add: *1014 = Tylenchus oryzae* van Breda de Haan, 1902

N—*gigus*
Oxydirus Jairajpuri, 1964 *936*

N—*ginglymodontus*
Anatonchus Mulvey, 1961 *1031*

N—*gisleni*
Plectus Allgén, 1951 *28a*
NOTE: regarded as *nomen dubium* by Maggenti, 1961 *1020*

A—*glischrus, Ditylenchus*
Add: *Neoditylenchus* (Rühm, 1956) Meyl, 1961 *1028*

N—*globiceps*
Mesodorylaimus Loof, 1964 *1001*

N—*globilabiatus*
Plectus Andrássy, 1963 *774*

A—*globilabiatus, Plectus* Kirjanova
Add: NOTE: regarded as *nomen dubium* by Maggenti, 1961 *1020*

N—*globulicola*
Pratylenchus Romaniko, 1960 *1053*

A—*glomerans, Tripyla*
Add: *806* syn: *Tripyla papillata*, var. *crystallifera* Micoletzky, 1922 (*c*)

29

806 syn: *Promonchus filipjevi* Micoletzky, 1923
806 syn?: *Tripyla lata* Cobb, 1914
806 syn?: *Tripyla papillata*, var.
cornuta of Andrássy, 1952

PAGE 57

C—*goettingiana, Heterodera*
Change footnote to *regarded as valid
name by Goodey, 1963 *881*

A—*goffarti, Bunonema*
1. Place asterisk before *Stammeria*
2. Add: *Bunonema   [Rhodolaimus]*
Sachs, 1949 *1055*
*valid genus according to Goodey,
1963 *881*

A—*goffarti, Criconema*
Add: *Criconemoides*   (Volz,   1951)
Oostenbrink, 1960 *1038*
891 = *Criconemoides   macrodorum*
Taylor, 1936
NOTE: placed in *species inquirendae*
by Siddiqi & Goodey, 1963 *1103*

A—*goffarti, Diplogaster*
Add: *Koerneria* (Körner, 1954) Meyl,
1961 *1028*

N—*gonzalezi*
Bursaphelenchus Loof, 1964 *1001*

N—*goodeyi*
Criconemoides de Guiran, 1963 *892*
Criconemella (de Guiran, 1963) de
Grisse & Loof, 1965 *891*
Neocriconema (de   Guiran,   1963)
Diab & Jenkins, 1965 *845*
Mesocriconema (de   Guiran,   1963)
Andrássy, 1965 *781b*

N—*goodeyi*
Criconemoides Jairajpuri, 1964 *938*
930 = *Criconemoides basili* Jairajpuri,
1964

A—*goodeyi, Cylindrocorpus*
Add: *Goodeyus*   (Rühm,   1959)
Goodey, 1963 *881*

N—*goodeyi*
Ecphyadophora Husain & Khan, 1965
915

N—*goodeyi*
Longidorus Hooper, 1961 *909*
909 syn: *Longidorus elongatus* of
Goodey, 1951

A—*goodeyi, Paratylenchus*
1. Place asterisk before *Paratylenchus*
2. Add: *Gracilacus*   (Oostenbrink,
1953) Raski, 1962 *1044*
*regarded as valid genus by Siddiqi
& Goodey, 1964 *1103*

A—*goodeyi, Pratylenchus*
Add: *993* syn: *Tylenchus musicola* of
Filipjev & Schuurmans Stekhoven,
1941
993 syn: *Anguillulina musicola* of
Goodey, 1932

A—*goodeyi, Rotylenchus*
1. Place asterisk before *Rotylenchus*
2. Place double asterisk before second
and fourth entries under *goodeyi*
3. Add: *regarded as valid genus by
Goodey & Seinhorst, 1960 *880* &
Sher, 1961 *1065*
**invalid synonymies according to
Goodey & Seinhorst, 1960 *880*

N—*goodeyi*
Tylenchorhynchus Marinari, 1962 *1022*

N—*goodeyi*
Tylenchus Das, 1960 *842*
Tylenchus [Filenchus] Das, 1960 *881*

N—*gossypii*
Axonchium de Coninck, 1962 *833*

A—*graciliformis, Rhabditis*
Add: NOTE: placed in *species inquirendae* by Meyl, 1961 *1028*

PAGE 58

A—*gracilis, Belonolaimus*
Add: *881* syn: *Belonolaimus longicaudatus* Rau, 1958

A—*gracilis, Diplogaster*
1. Place asterisk before *Diplogastrellus*
2. Add: *valid   genus   according   to
Meyl, 1961 *1028*

gracilis

A—*gracilis, Dorylaimus*
  Add: *Eudorylaimus* (de Man, 1876)
  Goodey, 1963 *881*

N—*gracilis*
  Helionema Brzeski, 1962 *793*

A—*gracilis, Hemicycliophora*
  Add: *1164 Hemicycliophora gracilis*
  of Zuckerman, 1961 = *Hemicyclio-*
  phora vaccinium Reed & Jenkins,
  1963

A—*gracilis, Psilenchus*
  Add: *881* = *Tylenchus* [*Filenchus*]
  neogracilis Goodey, 1963
  Basiria (Thorne, 1949) Siddiqi,
  1963 *1085*

N—*gracilis*
  Roqueus Thorne, 1964 *1133*

A—*gracilis, Tripyla*
  Add: NOTE: placed in *species inquiren-*
  dae by Meyl, 1961 *1028*

A—*gracilis, Tylenchus* Cobb
  Add: *876* syn: *Tylenchus cobbi* de
  Man, 1907
  NOTE: placed in *species inquirendae*
  by Goodey, 1960 *876*

A—*gracilis, Tylenchus* de Man
  Add: *Hirschmannia* (de Man, 1880)
  Luc & Goodey, 1962 *1014*
  Hirschmanniella (de Man, 1880)
  Luc & Goodey, 1964 *1015*

PAGE 59

A—*gracilis,* var. *octopapillata, Bastiania*
  Add: *1028* = *Bastiania octopapillata*
  Meyl, 1961

N—*gracillima*
  Actinca Andrássy, 1964 *781*
  781 syn: *Actinolaimus papillatus* of
  Altherr, 1960

A,C—*gracillima, Monhystera*
  1. Change de Man, 1921 *440* to Cobb,
  1894 *118*
  2. Add: *881 Monhystera gracillima* of
  de Man, 1921 = *Monhystera para-*
  gracillima Goodey, 1963

graminophilus

A—*graciloides, Diplogaster*
  Add: NOTE: placed in *species inquiren-*
  dae by Meyl, 1961 *1028*

A—*graciloides, Dorylaimus*
  Add: NOTE: placed in *species inquiren-*
  dae by Meyl, 1961 *1028*

A—*graciloides, Tylenchus*
  1. Place asterisk before *Tylenchus*
  [*Filenchus*]
  2. Add: *Filenchus* (Micoletzky, 1925)
  Meyl, 1961 *1028*
  *valid name according to Goodey,
  1963 *881*

N—*grahami*
  Plectus Allgén, 1951 *28a*
  NOTE: regarded as *nomen nudum* by
  Maggenti, 1961 *1020*

N—*graminicola*
  Meloidogyne Golden & Birchfield,
  1965 *871*

A,C—*graminicola, Tylenchorhynchus*
  1. Change species name to *gramini-*
  colus
  2. Add: NOTE: placed in *species in-*
  quirendae by Tarjan, 1964 *1125*

N—*graminis*
  Dorylaimellus Kruger, 1965 *989*

N—*graminis*
  Hypsoperine Sledge & Golden, 1964
  1116

A—*graminophila, Basiria*
  1. Place asterisk before *Basiria*
  2. Add: *Tylenchus* [*Filenchus*] (Siddiqi, 1959) Goodey, 1963 *881*
  *valid name according to Siddiqi,
  1963 *1085*

PAGE 60

A,C,T—*graminophilus, Anguillulina*
  1. Change species name to *gramino-*
  phila
  2. Transpose entire entry to immediately after *graminis, Vibrio*
  3. Add: *Anguina* (Goodey, 1933)
  Thorne, 1961 *1132*

A—graminum, Diplogaster
Add: NOTE: (2) placed in species inquirendae by Goodey, 1963 881

N—grande
Scutellonema Sher, 1964 1067

A—grande, Tylencholaimus
Add: NOTE: placed in species inquirendae by Meyl, 1961 1028

A—grandipapilloides, Trilobus
Add: Tobrilus (Micoletzky, 1922)
Meyl, 1961 1028

A—granulosus, Leptonchus
Add: 999 Leptonchus granulosus of
Loof & Oostenbrink, 1962 = Lepton-
chus scintillans Loof, 1964

A,C—granulosus, Plectus
1. Delete footnote
2. Delete granulosus from the seventh
line under specific name
3. Add: *valid genus according to
Goodey, 1951 293 and Paramonov,
1964 1040 but Maggenti, 1961 1020
regards Anaplectus as the correct
genus

N—grosmannae
Tylaphelenchus Rühm, 1965 1055c

N—guenini
Rhabditis Altherr, 1960 754

A—guernei, Eubostrichus
Add: 618 Criconema guernei of
Menzel, 1914 = Criconema menzeli
Stefánski, 1924 as entry between
Hoplolaimus and Iota

N—guevarai
Pratylenchoides Tobar Jiménez, 1963
1144
1129 syn: Zygotylenchus browni Siddiqi, 1963
1129 syn: Mesotylus gallicus de
Guiran, 1964

N—gulliver
Dorylaimus Andrássy, 1964 781

A—gulosus, Tylenchus
Add: 993 = Tylenchus   penetrans
Cobb, 1917
NOTE: Loof, 1961 996 states that
this species, and Tylenchus penetrans Cobb, 1917 are synony-
mous. However, he proposes that
gulosus be suppressed, circum-
venting the law of priority, and
that it be regarded a synonym of
T. penetrans.

N—gymnochilus
Tyleptus Loof, 1964 1001

N—habibullae
Cervidellus Erzhanov, 1964 852a

N—hallensis
Monhystera Meyl, 1961 1028
1028 syn: Monhystera multisetosa, var.
hallensis Paetzold, 1958

A—halleri, Rhabditolaimus
Add: Diplogasteroides (Fuchs, 1915)
Rühm, 1956 1028

A—halophilus, Neocephalobus
Add: 881 Neocephalobus halophilus
Paetzold,   1958 = Panagrolaimus
paetzoldi Goodey, 1963

A—halophilus, Panagrolaimus
Add: NOTE: placed in species inquirendae by Meyl, 1961 1028

N—hamata
Osstella Heyns, 1962 900

A—hamatus, Macrolaimus
1. Place asterisk before Macrolaimus
2. Add: *valid species according to
Sanwal, 1960 1057

A—hartingii, Dorylaimus
Add: Nygolaimus [Nygolaimus] (de
Man, 1880) Thorne, 1930 692 be-
tween entries Nygolaimus and
Dorylaimus [Nygolaimus]

N—hastatus
Eudorylaimus Andrássy, 1963 772
Enchodorella (Andrássy, 1963) Sid-
diqi, 1964 1090a

N—*hastatus*
    Sphaerularia Khan, 1957 *970*
    Stictylus (Khan, 1957) Khan, 1960 *973*
    Sphaerulariopsis (Khan, 1957) Nickle, 1963 *1036*

N—*hastatus*
    Tylencholaimus Siddiqi, 1964 *1092a*

N—*hastulatus*
    Belonolaimus Colbran, 1960 *830*
    Telotylenchus (Colbran, 1960) Jairajpuri, 1963 *928*

A—*hawaiiensis, Mononchus*
    Add: *1030 = Mononchus   [Mylonchulus] incurvus* Cobb, 1917

A,C—*hawaiiensis, Plectus*
    1. Delete asterisks and footnote
    2. Add: *1020 = Plectus   parietinus* Bastian, 1865

N—*hectographi*
    Cryptaphelenchus Rühm in Rühm and Chararas, 1957 *1056*

A—*hedickei, Dorylaimus*
    Add: *Dorylaimellus* Jairajpuri, 1964 *936*

A—*heideri, Criconema*
    Add: NOTE: placed in *incertae sedis* by de Grisse & Loof, 1965 *891*

A—*helenae, Bunonema*
    Add: *Bunonema* [*Aspidonema*] Sachs, 1949 *1055*
    Stammeria (Sachs, 1949) Goodey, 1963 *881*

N—*helicus*
    Aorolaimus Sher, 1963 *1066*

N—*helicus*
    Aphelenchoides Heyns, 1964 *905*

A—*helophilus, Pratylenchus*
    Add: *993 = Tylenchus   pratensis* de Man, 1880

N—*hemisphaericaudatus*
    Criconemoides Wu, 1965 *1160* (*c*)

Macroposthonia (Wu, 1965) de Grisse & Loof, 1965 *891*

A—*henrichae, Diplogaster*
    1. Place asterisk before *Allodiplogaster*
    2. Add: *valid genus according to Meyl, 1961 *1028*

N—*hercyniense*
    Criconemoides Kischke, 1956 *1028*
    1028 = Criconemoides   morgense   hercyniense Kischke, 1956
    NOTE: regarded *incertae sedis* by de Grisse & Loof, 1965 *891*

A—*hessei, Aphelenchus*
    Add: NOTE: placed in *species inquirendae* by Goodey, 1960 *876*

A—*hessi, Bunonema*
    1. Place asterisk before *Bunonema*
    2. Add: *valid name according to Goodey, 1963 *881*

A—*hessi, Diplogaster*
    Add: NOTE: placed in *species inquirendae* by Meyl, 1961 *1028*

A—*heterocercus, Dolichodorus*
    Add: *761 = Tylenchus   penetrans* Cobb, 1917

C—*heterophallus, Aphelenchoides*
    Delete asterisks and footnote

A,C—*heterospiculum, Cephalobus*
    1. Change 1951 *27* to 1950 *26*
    2. Add: *Cephalobus* [*Heterocephalobus*] Allgén, 1951 *786*

A—*heterurus, Dorylaimellus*
    Add: *Dorylaimus* (Schuurmans Stekhoven & Teunissen, 1938) Heyns, 1964 *906*

A—*heterurus, Myolaimus*
    Add: *1028* syn: *Macrolaimus maupasi* Hnatewytsch, 1929

N—*hexalineatus*
    Tylenchus Geraert, 1962 *864*
    Tylenchus [*Cephalenchus*] Geraert, 1962 *867* (*c*)

heynsi

867 syn: *Tylenchus* [*Cephalenchus*] *megacephalus* Goodey, 1962
832a = *Tylenchus emarginatus* Cobb, 1893

N—*heynsi*
  Cobbonchus Coetzee, 1965 *829*

N—*hilarus*
  Psilenchus Siddiqi, 1963 *1085*

N—*hintoni*
  Actinolaimus Lee, 1961 *991*

A—*hirschmannae, Diplogaster*
  Add: *Koerneria* (Sachs, 1950) Meyl, 1961 *1028*

PAGE 64

N—*hispalensis*
  Criconemoides Arias Delgado, López Pedregal, & Jiménez Millán, 1963 *783*
  Macroposthonia (Arias Delgado, López Pedregal, & Jiménez Millán, 1963) de Grisse & Loof, 1965 *891*

A—*histophorus, Diplogaster*
  Add: *Mononchoides* (Weingärtner in Körner, 1954) Goodey, 1963 *881*

A,C—*hofmaenneri, Dorylaimus*
  1. Delete asterisks and footnote
  2. Add: *Mesodorylaimus* (Menzel in Hofmänner & Menzel, 1914) Goodey, 1963 *881*

N—*holdemani*
  Peltamigratus Sher, 1964 *1068*

N—*hopedoroides*
  Enchodelus Altherr, 1963 *757*

N—*hopperi*
  Miconchus Mulvey, 1962 *1032*

N—*hortensis*
  Amphidelus Andrássy, 1961 *766*

N—*housei*
  Telotylenchus Raski, Prasad, & Swarup, 1964 *1045*

A—*hsuei, Prismatolaimus*
  Add: *761* = *Prismatolaimus intermedius* Bütschli, 1873

hylurginophila

A—*humuli, Heterodera*
  1. Place asterisk before *Heterodera*
  2. Add: *valid name according to Goodey, 1963 *881*

N—*hungaricum*
  Criconema Andrássy, 1962 *769a*

A—*hunti, Aphelenchoides*
  Add: NOTE: placed in *species inquirendae* by Goodey, 1960 *876*

A—*hyacinthi, Tylenchus*
  Add: *212* = *Ditylenchus dipsaci*, var. *hyacinthi* (Prillieux, 1881) Filipjev & Schuurmans Stekhoven, 1941

PAGE 65

N—*hyderabadensis*
  Aphelenchoides Das, 1960 *842*
  Seinura (Das, 1960) Goodey, 1960 *876*
  *regarded as valid genus and in *species inquirendae* by Hechler & Taylor, 1965 *897*

N—*hyderi*
  Boleodorus Husain & Khan, 1965 *919*

N—*hygrophilum*
  Criconemoides Goodey, 1963 *881*
  881 syn: *Criconema annulifer*, f. *hygrophilum* Andrássy, 1952
  Nothocriconema (Goodey, 1963) de Grisse & Loof, 1965 *891*
  781b = *Criconema stygia* Schneider, 1940

A—*hylastophilus, Aphelenchus*
  Add: *Ektaphelenchus* (Fuchs, 1930) Goodey, 1960 *876*
  876 syn: *Parasitaphelenchus hylastophilus*, f. *ateri* Fuchs, 1930

A—*hylastophilus*, f. *ateri, Parasitaphelenchus*
  Add: *876* = *Aphelenchus hylastophilus* (Fuchs, 1930) Filipjev, 1934

A—*hylobii, Diplogaster*
  Add: *Koerneria* (Fuchs, 1915) Meyl, 1961 *1028*

A—*hylurginophila, Fuchsia*
  Add: *Mikoletzkya* (Rühm, 1956) Baker, 1962 *784*

N—*ibiti*
Eudorylaimus Lordello, 1965 *1004a*

N—*icarus*
Tylenchorhynchus Wallace & Greet, 1964 *1144c*
1144c syn: *Anguillulina macrura* Goodey, 1932 in part
1144c syn: *Tylenchorhynchus macrurus* of Filipjev, 1936 in part
1144c syn: *Tylenchorhynchus macrurus* of Allen, 1955 in part

N—*idalimus*
Gracilacus Raski, 1962 *1044*
Paratylenchus (Raski, 1962) Siddiqi & Goodey, 1964 *1103*

A—*idius, Aphelenchoides*
Add: *Bursaphelenchus* (Rühm, 1956) Goodey, 1960 *876*

N—*ifacolum*
Xiphinema Luc, 1961 *1010*

A—*ignavus,* var. *colourus, Ironus*
Add: *1028* = *Ironus colourus* Meyl, 1961

A—*iheringi, Lycolaimus*
Add: NOTE: placed in *species inquirendae* by Goodey, 1963 *881*

A—*imamurae, Dorylaimus*
Add: *Mesodorylaimus* (Thorne & Swanger, 1936) Goodey, 1963 *881*

N—*imbricatum*
Criconema Colbran, 1965 *832b*

N—*imitator*
Dorylaimellus Heyns, 1964 *906*

N—*imitator*
Xiphinema Heyns, 1965 *908*

N—*impar*
Boleodorus Khan & Basir, 1964 *965*

A—*impar, Bunonema*
Add: *1055* = *Bunonema inequale* Cobb, 1915
Stammeria (Cobb, 1915) Goodey, 1963 *881*

N—*impar*
Longidorella Khan & Khan, 1964 *966*

A,C—*inaequidens, Diplogaster*
1. Delete asterisks and footnote
2. Add: *Metadiplogaster* (Paesler, 1946) Meyl, 1961 *1028*

A,C—*incae, Dorylaimus*
1. Delete asterisks and footnote
2. Add: *Mesodorylaimus* (Steiner, 1920) Goodey, 1963 *881*

A—*incisa, Anguillulina*
Add: NOTE: placed in *species inquirendae* by Andrássy, 1960 *761*

A,C—*incognata, Anguillulina*
1. Delete note
2. Add: *Chitinotylenchus* (van der Linde, 1938) Loof, 1956 *391*

A—*incognita, Oxyuris*
Add: *881* syn: *Meloidogyne incognita,* var. *acrita* Chitwood, 1949
881 syn: *Meloidogyne incognita incognita* (Kofoid & White, 1919) Chitwood, 1949

A—*incognita incognita, Meloidogyne*
Add: *881* = *Oxyuris incognita* Kofoid & White, 1919

A—*incognita,* var. *acrita, Meloidogyne*
Add: *881* = *Oxyuris incognita* Kofoid & White, 1919

N—*incultus*
Mononchus [*Cobbonchus*] Carvalho, 1960 *811a*

N—*incultus*
Rotylenchus Sher, 1965 *1071*

A—*incurvus, Aphelenchoides*
Add: *Bursaphelenchus* (Rühm, 1956) Goodey, 1960 *876*

A—*incurvus, Diplogaster*
Add: *Anchidiplogaster* (Körner, 1954) Meyl, 1961 *1028*
Diplogastrellus (Körner, 1954) Goodey, 1963 *881*

A—incurvus, Mononchus
Add: †*Mylonchulus* (Cobb, 1917)
Andrássy, 1958 *49d*
1030 syn: *Mononchus hawaiiensis*
Cassidy, 1931

PAGE 68

N—indica
Basiliophora Husain & Khan, 1965 *915*

N—indica
Hemicycliophora Siddiqi, 1961 *1077*

N—indicum
Axonchium Siddiqi, 1964 *1092a*

A—indicum, Xiphinema
Add: *1019* = *Xiphinema insigne* Loos, 1949

N—indicus
Aetholaimus Jairajpuri, 1965 *944*

N—indicus
Boleodorus Jairajpuri, 1962 *926*

N—indicus
Dorylaimellus Siddiqi, 1964 *1089*

N—indicus
Helicotylenchus Siddiqi, 1963 *1088*

N—indicus
Hoplolaimus Sher, 1963 *1066*

N—indicus
Pratylenchus Das, 1960 *842*

N—indicus
Proleptonchus Siddiqi & Khan, 1964 *1108*

N—indicus
Telotylenchus Siddiqi, 1960 *1073*

N—indicus
Tylenchorhynchus Siddiqi, 1961 *1078*
1086 = *Tylenchorhynchus brevilineatus* Williams, 1960

A—inequale, Bunonema
Add: *Bunonema* [*Rhodolaimus*] Cobb, 1915 *1055* (*c*)

1055 syn: *Bunonema impar* Cobb, 1915
Stammeria (Cobb, 1915) Goodey, 1963 *881*

A—inermis, Diplogaster
Add: NOTE: placed in *species inquirendae* by Meyl, 1961 *1028*

A—inermis, Leptodera
Add: *1028* syn: *Rhabditis inermoides* Völk, 1950
881 syn: *Rhabditis* [*Telorhabditis*] *inermis inermis* (Schneider, 1866) Oerley, 1880
881 syn: *Rhabditis* [*Telorhabditis*] *inermis inermoides* Völk, 1950

A—inermis inermis, Rhabditis
Add: *881* = *Leptodera inermis* Schneider, 1866

A—inermis inermoides, Rhabditis
Add: *881* = *Leptodera inermis* Schneider, 1866

A—inermoides, Rhabditis
Add: *1028* = *Leptodera inermis* Schneider, 1866

A—infirmus, Tylenchus
1. Place asterisk before *Tylenchus*
2. Add: *Lelenchus* (Andrássy, 1954) Meyl, 1961 *1028*
*valid name according to Goodey, 1963 *881*

A—inflata, Diplohystera
Add: *Monhystera* (Onorato-de Cillis, 1917) Goodey, 1963 *881*

A,C—informe, Hoplolaimus
1. Change species name to *informis*
2. Add: *Macroposthonia* (Micoletzky, 1922) de Grisse & Loof, 1965 *891*
891 syn: *Criconema anura* Kirjanova, 1948
891 syn: *Criconemoides flandriensis* de Grisse, 1964

N—ingens
Xiphinema Luc & Dalmasso, 1964 *1013*

36

PAGE 69

A—*innoxius, Acrobeles*
Add: *Cervidellus* (Kirjanova, 1951)
Meyl, 1961 *1028*

N—*innuptus*
Nothotylenchus Andrássy, 1961 *767*

N—*inobservabilis*
Anguillulina Kirjanova, 1938 *981*
Ditylenchus (Kirjanova, 1938) Kirjanova, 1961 *982*

A—*inquirendus, Plectus*
Add: *Proteroplectus* (Andrássy, 1958)
Paramonov, 1964 *1040*

N—*insigne*
Criconemoides Siddiqi, 1961 *1077*
Macroposthonia (Siddiqi, 1961) de
Grisse & Loof, 1965 *891*

A—*insigne, Xiphinema*
Add: *1019* syn: *Xiphinema indicum*
Siddiqi, 1959

N—*insignis*
Helicotylenchus Khan & Basir, 1964
977

A—*insignis, Plectus*
Add: NOTE: placed in *species inquirendae* by Maggenti, 1961 *1020*

A—*insolitus, Rhabditophanes*
1. Place asterisk before *556*
2. Add: *synonymy questioned by
Meyl, 1961 *1028*
NOTE: placed in *species inquirendae*
by Meyl, 1961 *1028*, but regarded a valid species by Goodey,
1963 *881*

A—*insons, Acrobeles*
Add: *Cervidellus* (Kirjanova, 1951)
Meyl, 1961 *1028*

A—*intactus, Tylenchus*
1. Place asterisk before *Tylenchus* on
line 1
2. Add: *valid name according to
Meyl, 1961 *1028*

N—*intermedia*
Micronema Pokrovskaya, 1964 *1043a*

A—*intermedia, Tripyla*
Add: *Paratripyla* (Bütschli, 1873)
Brzeski, 1964 *806*

A—*intermedius, Diplogaster*
Add: NOTE: placed in *species inquirendae* by Goodey, 1963 *881*

N—*intermedius*
Discolaimus Heyns & Lagerwey, 1965
908b

N—*intermedius*
Dorylaimoides Thorne, 1964 *1133*

A—*intermedius, Dorylaimus*
Add: *Nygolaimus* (de Man, 1880)
Loof, 1961 *995*
995 Dorylaimus intermedius of
Thorne & Swanger, 1936 = *Eudorylaimus circulifer* Loof, 1961

PAGE 70

N—*intermedius*
Gracilacus Raski, 1962 *1044*
Paratylenchus (Raski, 1962) Siddiqi
& Goodey, 1964 *1103*

A—*intermedius, Monhystera*
Add: *761* syn: *Prismatolaimus hsuei*
Wu & Hoeppli, 1929

A—*intermedius, Plectus*
1. Delete asterisks and footnote
2. Add: *1020* = *Plectus parietinus*
Bastian, 1865

N—*intermedius*
Rotylenchoides Luc, 1960 *1009*
Helicotylenchus (Luc, 1960) Siddiqi
and Husain, 1964 *1105*

A—*intermedius, var. alpestris, Dorylaimus*
Add: NOTE: placed in *species inquirendae* by Loof, 1961 *995*

A—*intertextus, Dorylaimus*
Add: *Eudorylaimus* (Thorne &
Swanger, 1936) Goodey, 1963 *881*

37

A–*intrastriatus, Dorylaimus*
Add: *Discolaimoides* (Loos, 1945)
Loof, 1964 *1001*

A–*ipidicola, Aphelenchoides*
1. Place asterisk before *Aphelenchoides*
2. Add: *Tylaphelenchus* (Rühm, 1956) Goodey, 1960 *876*
   °valid genus according to Meyl, 1961 *1028*

N–*irregularis*
Criconemoides de Grisse, 1964 *889*
Macroposthonia (de Grisse, 1964) de Grisse & Loof, 1965 *891*

N–*irregularis*
Pratylenchus Loof, 1960 *993*
993 syn: *Pratylenchus pratensis* of Paetzold, 1955
993 syn: *Pratylenchus* sp. of Paetzold, 1958

A–*isolae, Diplogaster*
Add: *Eudiplogaster* (Meyl, 1953) Meyl, 1961 *1028*
Mononchoides (Meyl, 1953) Goodey, 1963 *881*

N–*israeli*
Aorolaimus Sher, 1963 *1066*

PAGE 71

A–*italiae, Xiphinema*
Add: NOTE: placed in *species inquirendae* by Luc & Tarjan, 1963 *1019*

N–*italicus*
Mononchus Andrássy, 1959 *760*

A,C,T–*italicus, Neotylenchus*
1. Change species name to *italicum*
2. Transpose entire entry to immediately after *italiae, Xiphinema*
3. Add: *Scytaleum* (Meyl, 1954) Andrássy, 1961 *767*

N–*itanhaense*
Xiphinema Carvalho, 1962 *812*

N–*ivorensis*
Paratylenchus Luc & de Guiran, 1962 *1016*

A–*jairi, Mononchus*
Add: *Iotonchus* (Lordello, 1959) Clark, 1961 *816*

A–*jakobii, Bunonema*
Add: *Bunonema* [*Rhodolaimus*] Sachs, 1949 *1055*
Stammeria (Sachs, 1949) Goodey, 1963 *881*

N–*janae*
Diplogasteroides Massey, 1962 *1024*
Masseyus (Massey, 1962) Paramonov, 1964 *1040*

N–*japonica*
Brevibucca Yokoo & Ota, 1961 *1161*

A–*javanica, Heterodera*
1. Place asterisk before *Meloidogyne*
2. Add: *881* syn: *Meloidogyne javanica bauruensis* Lordello, *1956*
   881 syn: *Meloidogyne javanica javanica* (Treub, 1885) Chitwood, 1949
   °valid name according to Goodey, 1963 *881*

A–*javanica bauruensis, Meloidogyne*
Add: *881* = *Heterodera javanica* Treub, 1885

A–*javanica javanica, Meloidogyne*
Add: *881* = *Heterodera javanica* Treub, 1885

A–*javanicum, Craspedonema*
1. Place asterisk before *Craspedonema*
2. Add: °valid genus according to Goodey, 1963 *881*

N–*jonesi*
Basiliophora Husain & Khan, 1965 *915*

N–*jonesi*
Longidorus Siddiqi, 1962 *1080*

N–*judithae*
Panagrolaimus Massey, 1964 *1025a*

N–*judithae*
Tylenchorhynchus Andrássy, 1962 *769a*

A—*junctus, Dorylaimus*
Add: *1119* syn: *Dorylaimus carteri,* f. *pratens* sf. *diversicaudatum* of Franz, 1942

N—*juniperi*
Criconemoides Edward & Misra, 1964 *850*
Xenocriconemella (Edward & Misra, 1964) de Grisse & Loof, 1965 *891*

N—*kaczanowskii*
Cephalobus [*Heterocephalobus*] Brzeski, 1960 *786*
Heterocephalobus (Brzeski, 1960) Brzeski, 1961 *788*
Cephalobus Brzeski, 1960 *881*

N—*kanayaensis*
Hemicriconemoides Nakasono & Ichinohe, 1961 *1035*

N—*karakalpakensis*
Ditylenchus Erzhanov, 1964 *852a*

PAGE 72

N—*kashmirensis*
Basiria Jairajpuri, 1965 *939*

N—*keilini*
Dorylaimus Lee, 1961 *991*

A—*kenyanus, Plectus*
Add: *1020* = *Plectus longicaudatus* Bütschli, 1873

N—*kikuyensis*
Meloidogyne de Grisse, 1961 *883*

N—*killicki*
Anatonchus Clark, 1963 *826*

A—*kirifuri, Tylencholaimus*
Add: NOTE: placed in *species inquirendae* by Jairajpuri, 1965 *945*

N—*kirjanovae*
Criconema Krall, 1963 *988*
891 = *Hoplolaimus annulifer* de Man, 1921

N—*kirjanovae*
Criconemoides Andrássy, 1962 *769a* (c)

891 = *Macroposthonia annulata* de Man, 1880
Neocriconema (Andrássy, 1962) Diab & Jenkins, 1965 *845*

N—*kirjanovae*
Diphtherophora Ivanova, 1958 *923*

A—*kirjanovae, Tylenchus*
1. Place asterisk before *Tylenchus* [*Tylenchus*]
2. Add: *Tylenchus* Andrássy, 1954 *1028*
*valid name according to Goodey, 1963 *881*

N—*kischkei*
Tylenchus Meyl, 1961 *1028*
1028 syn: *Tylenchus davainei tenuis* Kischke, 1956

N—*kittenbergeri*
Hoplolaimus Andrássy, 1961 *766a*
1066 = *Tylenchorhynchus pararobustus* Schuurmans Stekhoven & Teunissen, 1938

A—*komabaensis, Criconema*
Add: NOTE: regarded *incertae sedis* by de Grisse & Loof, 1965 *891*

A—*kongoensis, Aphelenchus*
Add: NOTE: placed in *species inquirendae* by Goodey, 1960 *876*

N—*kovacsi*
Criconemoides Andrássy, 1963 *774*
Nothocriconema (Andrássy, 1963) de Grisse & Loof, 1965 *891*

N—*kreisi*
Anatonchus Meyl, 1961 *1028*
1028 syn: *Mononchus* [*Anatonchus*] *tridentatus* of Kreis, 1924

A—*krishnaraoi, Dorylaimus*
Add: *Mesodorylaimus* (Moorthy, 1938) Goodey, 1963 *881*

A—*krygeri, Dorylaimus*
Add: *Aporcelaimus* (Ditlevsen, 1928) Brzeski, 1962 *794*

labiata

A,C,T—*labiata*, *Diplogaster*
1. Change species name to *labiatus*
2. Transpose entire entry to immediately after *labiatum*, *Axonchium*
3. Add: *Diplogasteritus* (Cobb in Merrill & Ford, 1916) Goodey, 1963 *881*

N—*labiata*
Hemicycliophora Colbran, 1960 *830*

PAGE 73

N—*labiatus*
Dorylaimellus Thorne, 1964 *1133*

N—*labiatus*
Helicotylenchus Román, 1965 *1052*

A—*labiatus*, *Pseudorhabditis*
Add: *Panagrolaimus* (Kreis, 1929) Andrássy, 1960 *761*
Trilabiatus (Kreis, 1929) Goodey, 1963 *881*

A—*lacustris*, *Mononchus*
Add: †*Mylonchulus* (Cobb in Cobb, 1915) Andrássy, 1958 *49d*
NOTE: regarded a valid species by Mulvey, 1961 *1030*

A—*lacustris*, *Rhabditis*
Add: NOTE: placed in *species inquirendae* by Meyl, 1961 *1028*

A—*lambdiensis*, *Rhabditis*
1. Place asterisk before *Pelodera*
2. Add: *Cruznema* (Maupas, 1919) Thorne, 1961 *1132*
881 syn: *Epimenides extricatus* Gutierrez, 1949
NOTE: valid genus according to Goodey, 1963 *881*

PAGE 74

A—*lata*, *Tripyla*
Add: *806* = ? *Tripyla glomerans* Bastian, 1865

N—*laterale*
Criconema Khan & Siddiqi, 1964 *969*
Lobocriconema (Khan & Siddiqi, 1964) de Grisse & Loof, 1965 *891*

leptocephalus

C,T—*latus*, *Neotylenchus*
1. Change species name to *latum*
2. Transpose entire entry to directly after *latum*, *Discolaimium*

A—*lavabri*, *Radopholus*
Add: *1014* = *Tylenchorhynchus spinicaudatus* Schuurmans Stekhoven, 1944

N—*leiomerus*
Hoplolaimus de Guiran, 1963 *893*

N—*leiperi*
Leiperotylenchus Das, 1960 *842*
Rotylenchulus (Das, 1960) Loof & Oostenbrink, 1962 *1003*
881 = *Rotylenchulus reniformis* Linford & Oliveira, 1940

N—*leipogrammus*
Aorolaimus Sher, 1963 *1066*

N—*lenorum*
Galophinema Siddiqi, 1965 *1098*

A—*lentiforme*, *Ogma*
Add: *1103* *Criconema lentiforme* of de Coninck, 1945 = *Ogma tripum* Schuurmans Stekhoven & Teunissen, 1938

PAGE 75

A—*lepidotum*, *Criconema*
Add: NOTE: (1) not regarded a *Criconema* by Oostenbrink, 1960 *1038*
(2) placed in *species inquirendae* by Meyl, 1961 *1028*

N—*lepidura*
Monhystera Andrássy, 1963 *774*

A,C,T—*lepidus*, *Diplogaster*
1. Change species name to *lepida*
2. Transpose entry to directly after *leontopodii*, *Tylenchus*
3. Add: *Koerneria* (Andrássy, 1958) Meyl, 1961 *1028*

N—*lepidus*
Dorylaimoides Timm, 1964 *1140*

N—*leptocephalus*
Longidorus Hooper, 1961 *909*

leptonchoides

N—*leptonchoides*
Tylencholaimus Loof, 1964 *1001*

A—*leptonepia, Heterodera*
1. Place asterisk before *Heterodera* on first line
2. Add: *valid name according to Goodey, 1963 *881*

N—*leptosoma*
Eudorylaimus Altherr, 1963 *757*

A,C—*leptosoma, Tylenchus*
1. Delete asterisks and footnote
2. Place asterisk before *Tylenchus* [*Lelenchus*]
3. Add: *Lelenchus* (de Man, 1880) Meyl, 1961 *1028* *valid name according to Goodey, 1963 *881*

A—*leptospiculum, Diplogaster*
Add: *Mononchoides* (Weingärtner, 1955) Goodey, 1963 *881*

N—*leptura*
Dorylaimoides Siddiqi, 1965 *1096*

N—*leptus*
Tylenchus [*Cephalenchus*] Siddiqi, 1963 *1083*

N—*lespedezae*
Heterodera Golden & Cobb, 1963 *872*

N—*leuceilyma*
Heterodera DiEdwardo & Perry, 1964 *846*

A,C—*leuckarti, Rhabditolaimus*
1. Delete asterisks and footnote
2. Place asterisk before *Dirhabdilaimus*
3. Add: *Neodiplogasteroides* (Fuchs, 1915) Meyl, 1961 *1028* *valid genus according to Goodey, 1963 *881*

A—*leucocephalus, Neocephalobus*
1. Place asterisk before *Panagrellus*
2. Add: *valid name according to Sanwal, 1960 *1058*

limitaneum

A—*levidentus, Diplogaster*
Add: *Eudiplogasterium* (Weingärtner, 1955) Meyl, 1961 *1028*
Prosodontus (Weingärtner, 1955) Goodey, 1963 *881*

A—*lheritieri, Diplogaster*
Add: *Mesodiplogaster* (Maupas, 1919) Goodey, 1963 *881*
881 syn: *Pristionchus ottoi* Paramonov, 1952

A—*lignicolus, Tricephalobus*
Add: *Trilabiatus* (Körner, 1954) Goodey, 1963 *881*

A—*ligniperdae, Parasitaphelenchus*
Add: NOTE: placed in *species inquirendae* by Goodey, 1960 *876*

A—*ligniperdae, Plectonchus*
Add: NOTE: placed in *species inquirendae* by Meyl, 1961 *1028*, but regarded a valid species by Goodey, 1963 *881*

A—*lignophilus, Aphelenchoides*
Add: *Laimaphelenchus* (Körner, 1954) Goodey, 1960 *876*
Bursaphelenchus (Körner, 1954) Meyl, 1961 *1028*

N—*lilium*
Aphelenchoides Yokoo, 1964 *1160b*

A,C—*limicola, Rhabditis*
1. Change third and fourth lines under species name to: *189 Rhabditis* [*Rhabditis*] *limicola* of Osche, 1952 = *Rhabditis chitwoodi* Bassen, 1940
2. Add: *1028* = *Rhabditis chitwoodi* Bassen, 1940

A,C—*limitaneum, Criconema*
1. Change species name to *limitanea*
2. Add: *Criconemoides* (Luc, 1959) Luc & de Guiran, 1960 *1015a*
Discocriconemella (Luc, 1959) de Grisse & Loof, 1965 *891*
Neocriconema (Luc, 1959) Diab & Jenkins, 1965 *845* (*c*)

limnophilum

Mesocriconema (Luc, 1959) Andrássy, 1965 *781b*

A,C—limnophilum, Dorylaimus
1. Change species name to *limnophilus*
2. Add: *Dorylaimoides* (de Man, 1880) Loof, 1964 *1001*

N—lindbergi
Eudorylaimus Andrássy, 1960 *762*

N—lineatus
Belonolaimus Román, 1964 *1051a*

A—lineatus, Diplogaster
Add: *Diplogasteritus* (Fuchs, 1915) Meyl, 1961 *1028*
Mikoletzkya (Fuchs, 1915) Baker, 1962 *784*
Acrostichus (Fuchs, 1915) Massey, 1962 *1024*
*valid genus according to Goodey, 1963 *881*

A—lineum, Anguillula
Add: NOTE: placed in *species inquirendae* by Meyl, 1961 *1028*

A—linfordi, Aphelenchoides
Add: *Seinura* (Christie, 1939) Goodey, 1960 *876*

N—linfordi
Neotylenchus Hechler, 1962 *895*

N—lingualis
Hemicycliophora Kannan, 1961 *958*
NOTE: placed in *species inquirendae* by Siddiqi & Goodey, 1964 *1103*

A—lingulatum, Stephanium
Add: NOTE: (2) regarded as in the Nygolaiminae by Andrássy, 1960 *761*

A—linocerca, Diplogaster
Add: *Fictor* (Völk, 1950) Goodey, 1963 *881*

A,C—linstowii, Diplogaster
1. Delete lines 7 and 8
2. Place asterisk before *484*
3. Add: *Diplogaster* *linstowii* of Fuchs, 1915 regarded *incertae sedis* by Baker, 1962 *784*

longicauda

PAGE 78

A,C—liratus, Leptodera
1. In line 7 under species name change 1866 to 1886
2. Place asterisk before *Diplogasteritus*
3. Add: *valid genus according to Goodey, 1963 *881*
NOTE: placed in *species inquirendae* by Meyl, 1961 *1028*

N—litchi
Hemicriconemoides Edward & Misra, 1964 *851*

N—litoralis
Paracephalobus Akhtar, 1962 *752*

A—littoralis, Aphelenchus
Add: NOTE: placed in *species inquirendae* by Goodey, 1960 *876*

A—lobatum, Criconemoides
Add: *891* = *Criconema rusticum* Micoletzky, 1915

N—lobatus
Trichodorus Colbran, 1965 *832c*

N—loeffleri
Dorylaimus Andrássy, 1964 *781*
781 syn: *Dorylaimus filiformis* of Allgén, 1952 in part

A—longicauda, Cephalonema
Add: *Ironus* (Cobb, 1893) Goodey, 1963 *881*

A—longicauda, Diplogaster Claus
Add: NOTE: placed in *species inquirendae* by Meyl, 1961 *1028*

A—longicauda, Diplogaster Rahm
Add: NOTE: placed in *species inquirendae* by Goodey, 1963 *881*

N—longicauda
Monhystera Daday, 1899 *174*
Prismatolaimus (Daday, 1899) Milne, 1963 *1029*
Onchulus (Daday, 1899) Andrássy, 1964 *780*
780 syn: *Onchulus longicaudatus* Cobb, 1920

longicaudata

A,C—*longicaudata, Hemicycliophora*
1. Delete note
2. Add: *Caloosia* (Loos, 1948) Siddiqi & Goodey, 1964 *1103*
   1103 Hemicycliophora longicaudata of Siddiqi, 1961 = *Caloosia paralongicaudata* Siddiqi & Goodey, 1963

N—*longicaudatum*
Doryllium Loof, 1964 *1001*

N—*longicaudatum*
Xiphinema Luc, 1961 *1010*

A,C,T—*longicaudatus, Aphelenchus*
1. Change species name to *longicaudata*
2. Transpose entire entry to immediately after *longicauda*, var. *fructicola, Rhabditidoides*
3. Delete asterisks and footnote
4. Add: *Seinura* (Cobb, 1893) Goodey, 1960 *876*

A—*longicaudatus, Belonolaimus*
Add: *881* = *Belonolaimus gracilis* Steiner, 1949

C—*longicaudatus, Cephalobus*
In the fourth and fifth lines under the species name delete parentheses and Steiner, 1936

N—*longicaudatus*
Dorylaimellus Jairajpuri, 1964 *936*

N—*longicaudatus*
Longidorus Siddiqi, 1962 *1080*

A—*longicaudatus, Onchulus*
Add: *780* = *Monhystera longicauda* Daday, 1899

N—*longicaudatus*
Panagrolaimus Sumenkova, 1965 *1121b*

A—*longicaudatus, Plectus*
Add: *761* syn: *Plectus chengmohliangi* Hoeppli & Chu, 1932
1020 syn: *Plectus kenyanus* Allgén, 1952
Proteroplectus (Bütschli, 1873) Paramonov, 1964 *1040*

longula

A—*longicaudatus, Pristionchus*
Add: NOTE: placed in *species inquirendae* by Goodey, 1963 *881*

N—*longicaudatus*
Tridontus Khera, 1965 *979*

N—*longicollis*
Dorylaimellus Loof, 1964 *1001*

N—*longicollis*
Eudorylaimus Brzeski, 1964 *805*

A—*longicollis, Mononchus*
Add: NOTE: placed in *species inquirendae* by Clark, 1960 *815*

N—*longidoroides*
Xiphinema Luc, 1961 *1010*

N—*longimarginatus*
Trophurus Román, 1962 *1051*

A—*longisetosus, Diplogaster*
1. Place asterisk before *Fictor*
2. Add: *Holodiplogaster* (Paesler, 1946) Meyl, 1961 *1028*
   881 = *Diplogaster vorax* Goodey, 1929
   °valid genus according to Andrássy, 1964 *775*

A—*longispiculus, Diplogasteroides*
Add: *Rhabdontolaimus* (Meyl, 1954) Meyl, 1961 *1028*
NOTE: placed in *species inquirendae* by Goodey, 1963 *881*

N—*longistylus*
Trichodorus Yokoo, 1964 *1160d*

N—*longiurus*
Aphelenchoides Das, 1960 *842*

N—*longiurus*
Dorylaimoides Siddiqi, 1965 *1098*

A,C—*longula, Criconema*
1. Change species name to *longulum*
2. Add: *Criconemoides* (Gunhold, 1953) Oostenbrink, 1960 *1038* (*c*)

Nothocriconema (Gunhold, 1953) de Grisse & Loof, 1965 *891*
891 syn: *Criconema elegantula* Gunhold, 1953

PAGE 81

N—*loosi*
Pratylenchus Loof, 1960 *993*
993 syn: *Pratylenchus coffeae* of Loos, 1953

N—*lotharingiae*
Eudorylaimus Altherr, 1963 *755*

A—*lucani, Diplogaster*
Add: *Koerneria* (Körner, 1954) Meyl, 1961 *1028*

N—*luci*
Mesodorylaimus Brzeski & Szczygiel, 1961 *808*

N—*luci*
Peltamigratus Sher, 1964 *1068*

A—*luganensis, Dorylaimus*
Add: NOTE: placed in *species inquirendae* by Meyl, 1961 *1028*

N—*lutosus*
Longidorus Heyns, 1965 *908a*

A—*luziae, Diplogaster*
Add: *Koerneria* (Körner, 1954) Meyl, 1961 *1028*

N—*macbethi*
Peltamigratus Sher, 1964 *1068*

N—*machadoi*
Aglenchus Andrássy, 1963 *772*

A—*macramphis, Dorylaimus*
Add: *Nordia* (Altherr, 1950) Jairajpuri & Siddiqi, 1964 *950*
Enchodorella (Altherr, 1950) Siddiqi, 1964 *1090a*

A—*macrobolbus, Aphelenchus*
Add: *876* = *Aphelenchus avenae* Bastian, 1865

A—*macrobulbosus, Aphelenchoides*
Add: *Cryptaphelenchoides* (Rühm, 1956) Goodey, 1960 *876*

A—*macrocerca, Rhabditis*
Add: *881* = *Pelodera axei* Cobbold, 1884

PAGE 82

A,C,T—*macrodorum, Criconemoides*
1. Change species name to *macrodora*
2. Transpose entire entry to directly after *macrodon, Diplogaster*
3. Add: *Xenocriconemella* (Taylor, 1936) de Grisse & Loof, 1965 *891*
891 syn: *Criconema goffarti* Volz, 1951

N—*macrodorus*
Paratylenchus Brzeski, 1963 *802*

A,C—*macrolaimus, Dorylaimus*
1. Delete asterisks and footnote
2. Add: *Paractinolaimus* (de Man, 1880) Andrássy, 1964 *781*

N—*macrolobata*
Criconemoides Jairajpuri & Siddiqi, 1963 *948*
Macroposthonia (Jairajpuri & Siddiqi, 1963) de Grisse & Loof, 1965 *891*

N—*macromucronatus*
Longidorus Siddiqi, 1962 *1080*

N—*macrophallus*
Tylencholaimellus Thorne, 1964 *1133*

A—*macrophallus, Tylenchus*
Add: *866 Tylenchus macrophallus* de Man, 1880 (females only) = *Paratylenchus microdorus* Andrássy, 1959
NOTE: (1) designated *incertae sedis* by Tarjan, 1960 *1124*
(2) placed in *species inquirendae* by Goodey, 1963 *881*

PAGE 83

N—*macroproctus*
Dorylaimus Altherr, 1963 *755*

N—*macrosoma*
Longidorus Hooper, 1961 *909*

C—*macrospiculatum, Hexatylus*
Delete asterisks and footnote

A—*macrospiculatus, Rhabditis*
Add: NOTE: placed in *species inquiren-dae* by Meyl, 1961 *1028*

A—*macrospiculum, Diplogaster*
Add: *Anchidiplogaster* (Altherr, 1938)
Meyl, 1961 *1028*
NOTE: regarded *species inquirenda*
by Goodey, 1963 *881*

N—*macrostylus*
Ektaphelenchus Khan, 1960 *972*

A—*macrurus, Anguillulina*
Add: *1144c Anguillulina macrura*
Goodey, 1932 in part; *Tylen-chorhynchus macrurus* of Filipjev,
1936 and Allen, 1955 in part =
Tylenchorhynchus icarus Wallace
and Greet, 1964

PAGE 84

A—*macrurus, Cylindrolaimus*
Add: NOTE: (2) placed in *species in-quirendae* by Goodey, 1963 *881*

A—*macrurus, Diplogaster*
Add: NOTE: placed in *species inquiren-dae* by Goodey, 1963 *881*

A—*macrurus, Prismatolaimus*
Add: *881 = Monhystera dadayi*
Goodey, 1963

N—*macrurus*
Tylencholaimus Siddiqi, 1964 *1093a*

N—*madrasi*
Mononchus [*Mylonchulus*] Kannan,
1961 *956*

N—*madrasicum*
Bunonema Kannan, 1960 *955*

A—*magnidens, Psilenchus*
1. Place asterisk before *Psilenchus*
2. Add: *Tylenchus* [*Filenchus*]
(Thorne, 1949) Goodey, 1963 *881*
*valid name according to Siddiqi,
1963 *1085*

C—*magnificus, Chronogaster*
Change species name to *magnifica*

A—*magnificus, Heterodorus*
Add: *Enchodelus* (Altherr, 1952)
Goodey, 1963 *881*

N—*magniphasmum*
Scutellonema Sher, 1964 *1067*

N—*magnoliae*
Criconemoides Edward & Misra, 1964
850
891 = Criconemoides mutabile Taylor, 1936

N—*magnus*
Anaplectus Brzeski, 1963 *803*

N—*magnus*
Oxydirus Timm, 1964 *1140*

A,C—*magnus, Rhabditolaimus*
1. Delete asterisks and footnote
2. Add: *Rhabdontolaimus* (Völk,
1950) Meyl, 1961 *1028*

A—*major, Discolaimus*
1. Place asterisk before *50b* on line 2
2. Add: *synonymy not recognized by
Loof, 1964 *1001*

A,C—*major, Tylenchus*
1. Delete asterisks and footnote
2. Add: *Neoditylenchus* (Fuchs,
1915) Meyl, 1961 *1028*

PAGE 85

N—*makrodemas*
Plectus Massey, 1964 *1025a*

A—*makrodorum, Dorylaimus*
Add: NOTE: placed in *species inquiren-dae* by Meyl, 1961 *1028*

N—*maksymovi*
Eudorylaimus Altherr, 1963 *757*

A—*mali, Seinura*
1. Place asterisk before *Seinura*
2. Add: *valid genus according to
Goodey, 1960 *876*

A—*mammillatum, Xiphinema*
1. Place asterisk before *Xiphinema*
2. Add: *Longidorus* (Schuurmans (c)

45

Stekhoven & Teunissen, 1938)
Goodey, 1963 *881*
*valid genus according to Luc &
Tarjan, 1963 *1019*

A—*mangenoti, Tylenchulus*
Add: *Trophotylenchulus* (Luc, 1957)
Goodey, 1963 *881*

N—*mangiferae*
Hemicriconemoides Siddiqi, 1961 *1077*
1103 = *Iota squamosus* Cobb, 1913

N—*mangiferae*
Scutellonema Khan & Basir, 1965 *978*

N—*mangiferi*
Diphtherophora Husain, Khan, &
s'Jacob, 1965 *921*

N—*mangiferum*
Criconema Edward & Misra, 1963 *847*

A—*manifestus, Acrobeles*
Add: *Cervidellus* (Kirjanova, 1951)
Meyl, 1961 *1028*
NOTE: placed in *species inquirendae*
by Meyl, 1961 *1028*, but regarded
a valid species by Goodey, 1963
881

N—*maorium*
Pungentus Clark, 1963 *825*

N—*maracaiensis*
Pungentus Lordello, 1965 *1004a*

N—*maragnus*
Iotonchus Clark, 1961 *816*

N—*margaretae*
Panagromacra Massey, 1964 *1025a*

A—*marina, Rhabditis*
Add: *922* syn: *Rhabditis velata* Bres-
slau & Schuurmans Stekhoven in
Schuurmans Stekhoven, 1935
922 syn: *Rhabditis marina*, var.
danica Allgén, 1933
922 syn: *Rhabditis marina*, var.
kielensis Schulz, 1932
922 syn: *Rhabditis marina*, var.
nidrosiensis Allgén, 1933
922 syn: *Rhabditis marina*, var.
norwegica Allgén, 1933 (*c*)

922 syn: *Rhabditis marina*, var.
septentrionalis Steiner, 1916
922 syn: *Rhabditis fluviatilis* Bütschli, 1876
922 syn: *Rhabditis marina marina*
Bastian, 1865

A—*marina marina, Rhabditis*
Add: *922* = *Rhabditis marina* Bastian,
1865

A—*marina*, var. *bengalensis, Rhabditis*
Add: *Pellioditis* (Timm, 1956) Timm,
1960 *1135*
922 = *Rhabditis bengalensis* Inglis
& Coles, 1961

A—*marina*, var. *danica, Rhabditis*
Add: *922* = *Rhabditis marina* Bastian,
1865

A—*marina*, var. *kielensis, Rhabditis*
Add: *922* = *Rhabditis marina* Bastian,
1865

A—*marina*, var. *nidrosiensis, Rhabditis*
Add: *922* = *Rhabditis marina* Bastian,
1865

A—*marina*, var. *norwegica, Rhabditis*
Add: *922* = *Rhabditis marina* Bastian,
1865

A—*marina*, var. *septentrionalis, Rhabditis*
Add: *922* = *Rhabditis marina* Bastian,
1865

PAGE 86

C—*marinus, Tripyla*
1. Delete asterisks and footnote
2. Delete note

C—*marionis, Rhabditis*
In line 1 under species name change
1900 *445* to 1899 *444*

N—*maritima*
Criconemoides de Grisse, 1964 *889*
Macroposthonia (de Grisse, 1964) de
Grisse & Loof, 1965 *891*

N—*maritimus*
Belonolaimus Rau, 1963 *1046*

N—marshalli
Diplogasteroides Massey, 1962 *1024*

A—martinii, Aphelenchoides
Add: Ruehmaphelenchus (Rühm, 1955) Goodey, 1963 *881*

N—marylandicus
*Paratylenchus Jenkins, 1960 *951*
Gracilacus (Jenkins, 1960) Raski, 1962 *1044*
866 syn: Gracilacus capitatus Adams & Eichenmuller, 1962
*valid genus according to Siddiqi & Goodey, 1964 *1103*

N—mashhoodi
Tylenchorhynchus Siddiqi & Basir, 1959 *1099*

A,C—maupasi, Diplogaster
1. Delete asterisks and footnote
2. Add: Mesodiplogaster (Potts, 1910) Goodey, 1963 *881*

A—maupasi, Macrolaimus
Add: Myolaimus (Hnatewytsch, 1929) Sanwal, 1960 *1057*
1028 = Myolaimus heterurus Cobb, 1920

A—mauritianus, Mononchus
Add: Cobbonchus (Williams, 1958) Clark, 1960 *815a*

N—mauritiensis
Criconemoides Williams, 1960 *1147*
Discocriconemella (Williams, 1960) de Grisse & Loof, 1965 *891*

N—maximus
Aphelenchus Das, 1960 *842*

A—maximus, Dorylaimus
Add: *923* Longidorus maximus of Meyl, 1954 = Longidorus meyli Sturhan, 1963
Paralongidorus (Bütschli, 1874) Siddiqi, 1964 *1094*

N—medicaginis
Ditylenchus Wasilewska, 1965 *1145a*

N—megacephalus
Tylenchus [Cephalenchus] Goodey, 1962 *878*
867 = Tylenchus hexalineatus Geraert, 1962
832a = Tylenchus emarginatus Cobb, 1893

A—megadorus, Aphelenchoides
Add: Megadorus (Allen, 1941) Goodey, 1960 *876*

A—megalaimus, Mononchus
Add: Mononchus Cobb, 1917 *881*

A—melisi, Pelodera
Add: Pelodera [Cruznema] Marinari, 1957 *1028*

N—menthasolanus
Longidorus Konicek & Jensen, 1961 *986*
1080 = Dorylaimus elongatus de Man, 1876

A—menzeli, Hoplolaimus
Add: *618* syn: Criconema guernei of Menzel, 1914 as entry between entries Hoplolaimus and Iota

N—meridianus
Mesodorylaimus Andrássy, 1963 *774*

A—meridionalis, Plectus
Add: NOTE: placed in *species inquirendae* by Meyl, 1961 *1028*

A,C—merogaster, Dorylaimus
1. Delete asterisks and footnote
2. Add: Mesodorylaimus (Steiner, 1916) Goodey, 1963 *881*

N—mesadonus
Mononchus Clark, 1960 *814*

N—mettleri
Hemicycliophora Jenkins & Reed, 1964 *952*

N—meyli
Alaimus Andrássy, 1961 *766*

N—*meyli*
Aulolaimus Loof, 1961 *995*
995 syn: *Aulolaimus oxycephalus* of
Meyl, 1954

A—*meyli, Dorylaimus*
1. Place asterisk before *Dorylaimus*
2. Add: *valid genus according to
Goodey, 1963 *881*

N—*meyli*
Longidorus Sturhan, 1963 *1118*
1118 syn: *Longidorus maximus* of
Meyl, 1954

A—*micoletzkyi, Hemicycliophora*
Add: NOTE: placed in *species inquirendae* by Siddiqi & Goodey, 1964 *1103*

A—*micoletzkyi, Mononchus*
Add: *Prionchuloides* (Meyl, 1954)
Mulvey, 1963 *1034*

A—*micoletzkyi, Paraphelenchus*
Add: *879* = *Aphelenchus avenae* Bastian, 1865

PAGE 89

A—*micoletzkyi, Tylenchus*
1. Place asterisk before *Tylenchus*
2. Add: *Lelenchus* (Andrássy, 1954)
Baker, 1962 *784*
*valid name according to Goodey,
1963 *881*
NOTE: placed in *species inquirendae*
by Meyl, 1961 *1028*

A—*microcercus, Diplogaster*
Add: NOTE: placed in *species inquirendae* by Goodey, 1963 *881*

N—*microdorum*
Criconema de Grisse, 1964 *886*
Criconemoides (de Grisse, 1964) de
Grisse, 1964 *889*
Macroposthonia (de Grisse, 1964) de
Grisse & Loof, 1965 *891*
Neocriconema (de Grisse, 1964) Diab
& Jenkins, 1965 *845*
Mesocriconema (de Grisse, 1964) Andrássy, 1965 *781b*

A—*microdorus, Dorylaimus*
Add: *Longidorella* (de Man, 1880)
Goodey, 1963 *881* (*c*)

Nordia (de Man, 1880) Jairajpuri &
Siddiqi, 1964 *950*
Enchodorella (de Man, 1880)
Siddiqi, 1964 *1090a*

N—*microdorus*
Enchodelus Schiemer, 1965 *1061b*

A—*microdorus, Paratylenchus*
Add: *809* syn: *Paratylenchus brevihastus* Wu, 1962
866 syn: *Tylenchus macrophallus* de
Man, 1880 (females only)

A—*microlaimus, Aphelenchus*
Add: NOTE: placed in *species inquirendae* by Goodey, 1960 *876*

N—*microlaimus*
Paralongidorus Siddiqi, 1964 *1094*

C—*microphasmis, Tylenchus*
1. Change *Tylenchus* to *Tylenchorhynchus*
2. Change 1959 to 1960

A—*microstoma, Diplogaster*
Add: *Diplogasteritus* (Goodey, 1929)
Meyl, 1961 *1028*

A—*microstomus, Prismatolaimus*
Add: *Aphanolaimus* (Daday, 1905)
Goodey, 1963 *881*

A—*micrurus, Mononchus*
Add: NOTE: placed in *species inquirendae* by Mulvey, 1961 *1030*

A—*mikoletzkyi, Diplogaster*
Add: NOTE: placed in *species inquirendae* by Meyl, 1961 *1028*

PAGE 90

A—*mikuschi, Diplogaster*
1. Place asterisk before *Diplogastrellus*
2. Add: *valid genus according to
Meyl, 1961 *1028*

N—*millefolii*
Heterodera Kirjanova & Krall, 1965
985a

A—*minima, Diplogaster*
Add: NOTE: placed in *species inquirendae* by Goodey, 1963 *881*

A—*minimus, Acrobeles*
Add: *Cervidellus* (Thorne, 1925)
Goodey, 1963 *881*

N—*minimus*
Acrostichus Lazarevskaja, 1964 *990b*
Filipjevella (Lazarevskaja, 1964)
Lazarevskaja, 1965 *990c*

A—*minimus, Aphelenchoides*
Add: NOTE: placed in *species inquirendae* by Goodey, 1960 *876*, but regarded a valid species by Meyl,
1961 *1028*

A—*minimus, Plectus*
Add: NOTE: placed in *species inquirendae* by Maggenti, 1961 *1020*

A—*minor, Aphelenchus*
Add: NOTE: placed in *species inquirendae* by Goodey, 1960 *876*

N—*minor*
Cephalobus Kannan, 1960 *955*

A—*minor, Diplogaster* Cobb
Add: NOTE: placed in *species inquirendae* by Goodey, 1963 *881*

N—*minor*
Doryllium Jairajpuri, 1964 *932*

A—*minor, Iota*
Add: NOTE: placed in *species inquirendae* by Siddiqi & Goodey, 1964
1103

N—*minor*
Psilenchus Siddiqi, 1963 *1082*

A—*minor, Triplonchium*
Add: *Tylolaimophorus* (Thorne, 1939)
Goodey, 1963 *881*

N—*minusculus*
Paratylenchus Tarjan, 1960 *1124*

N—*minuta*
Paratripyla Brzeski, 1964 *806*

A—*minutissimus, Dorylaimus*
Add: †*Eudorylaimus* (Altherr, 1950)
Andrássy, 1959 *50d*
NOTE: regarded a valid species by
Goodey, 1963 *881*

N—*minutum*
Scutellonema Sher, 1964 *1067*

N—*minutus*
Diphtherophora Ivanova, 1958 *923*

N—*minutus*
Hemicriconemoides Esser, 1960 *853*
Hemicycliophora (Esser, 1960)
Goodey, 1963 *881*
*valid genus according to Siddiqi &
Goodey, 1964 *1103*

A—*minutus, Paratylenchus*
Add: *1124 = Paratylenchus elachistus*
Steiner, 1949

N—*minutus*
Sporonchulus Mulvey, 1963 *1034*

A,C—*minutus, Tylenchus*
1. Delete asterisks and footnote
2. Place asterisk before *Tylenchus*
[*Lelenchus*]
3. Add: *Lelenchus* (Cobb, 1893)
Meyl, 1961 *1028*
*valid name according to Goodey,
1963 *881*

A—*minyus, Pratylenchus*
Add: *993 = Aphelenchus neglectus*
Rensch, 1924

N—*mira*
Dorella Jairajpuri, 1964 *931*

N—*mirabile*
Elaphonema Heyns, 1962 *899*

A,C *mirabilis, Dorylaimellus*
1. In the second line of the note, delete "1876"
2. Add: *995 = Tylencholaimus brevicaudatus* (Tarjan, 1953) Tarjan,
1956
881 Dorylaimellus mirabilis of
Goodey, 1951 = *Dorylaimellus demani* Goodey, 1963

A—*mirabilis, Tylenchus*
Add: *881 Tylencholaimus mirabilis* of
de Man, 1876, 1880 & 1884 =
Dorylaimellus demani Goodey, 1963
945 syn: *Discomyctus brevicaudatus*
Tarjan, 1953

N—*mirus*
Boleodorus Khan, 1964 *960*

N—*mirus*
Ditylenchus Siddiqi, 1963 *1082*

N—*mirus*
Gracilacus Raski, 1962 *1044*
Paratylenchus (Raski, 1962) Siddiqi
& Goodey, 1964 *1103*

N—*mirzai*
Aphelenchus Das, 1960 *842*

A—*modestus, Aphelenchus*
Add: NOTE: placed in *species inquirendae* by Goodey, 1960 *876*

A—*modestus, Diplogaster*
Add: *Metadiplogaster* (Weingärtner,
1955) Meyl, 1961 *1028*
Demaniella (Weingärtner, 1955)
Goodey, 1963 *881*

N—*modestus*
Dorylaimoides Siddiqi, 1965 *1096*

N—*mombucae*
Metaporcelaimus Lordello, 1965 *1004a*

N—*mongolense*
Criconemoides Andrássy, 1964 *778*

N—*monhystera*
Butlerius Taylor, 1964 *1130*

N—*monhystera*
Discolaimium Siddiqi, 1965 *1098*

PAGE 93

A—*monhysteroides, Diplogaster*
1. Place asterisk before *Diplogastrellus*
2. Add: *valid genus according to
Meyl, 1961 *1028*

N—*monohystera*
Amphidelus Heyns, 1962 *898*

N—*monohystera*
Drepanodorus Brzeski, 1964 *805*

A—*monohystera, Longidorus*
Add: *1118* = *Dorylaimus elongatus* de
Man, 1876

A,C—*monohystera, Tripyla*
1. Delete asterisks and footnote
2. Add: *Trischistoma* (de Man,
1880) Schuurmans Stekhoven, 1951
590
Tripylina (de Man, 1880) Brzeski,
1963 *800*
*valid genus according to Brzeski,
1965 *807*

A—*monohystera,* var. *longicauda, Tripyla*
Add: NOTE: regarded *varietas inquirendum* by Brzeski, 1964 *806*

A—*monohysteroides, Rhabditis*
Add: NOTE: valid species according to
Meyl, 1961 *1028*

N—*monoplanus*
Discolaimus Heyns, 1963 *902*

A—*montanus, Mononchus*
Add: †*Mylonchulus* (Thorne, 1924)
Andrássy, 1958 *49d*
NOTE: regarded a valid species by
Mulvey, 1961 *1030*

N—*montanus,* var. *trionchulus*
Mononchus [*Mylonchulus*] Kannan,
1961 *957*

N—*monticolus*
Dorylaimellus Clark, 1963 *825*

N—*montserrati*
Criconemoides Arias Delgado, Jiménez
Millán, & López Pedregal, 1965 *782*

N—*morbidus*
Eudorylaimus Loof, 1964 *1001*

A—*morgense, Criconema*
Add: NOTE: regarded as *species inquirenda* by de Grisse & Loof, 1965
891

A—*morgense hercyniensis, Criconemoides*
Add: *1028* = *Criconemoides her-cyniensis* Kischke, 1956

A—*moro, Laimaphelenchus*
1. Place asterisk before *Laimaphelenchus*
2. Add: *valid genus according to Goodey, 1960 *876*

PAGE 94

N—*mosellae*
Eudorylaimus Altherr, 1963 *755*

N—*mothi*
Heterodera Khan & Husain, 1965 *959a*

N—*mozammili*
Nygellus Jairajpuri, 1965 *942*

N—*mpoumensis*
Actinolaimus Altherr, 1960 *753*

A—*mucronatus, Alaimus*
Add: *1028* = *Alaimus primitivus* de Man, 1880
NOTE: placed in *species inquirendae* by Meyl, 1961 *1028*

A—*mucronatus, Aphelenchoides*
Add: *Seinura* (Paesler, 1946) Goodey, 1960 *876*
NOTE: placed in *species inquirendae* by Hechler & Taylor, 1965 *897*

N—*mucronatus*
Cephalobus Kozlowska & Roguska-Wasilewska, 1963 *987*

N—*mucronatus*
Helicotylenchus Siddiqi, 1964 *1090*

N—*mucronatus*
Radopholus Das, 1960 *842*
1014 = *Tylenchus oryzae* v. Breda de Haan, 1902

N—*mucurubanus*
Discolaimus Loof, 1964 *1001*

C—*multicinctus, Tylenchus*
Delete asterisks and footnote

A—*multidentatus, Panagrolaimoides*
1. Place asterisk before *Panagrolaimoides*
2. Add: *Panagrolaimus* (Ivanova, 1958) Goodey, 1963 *881*
*valid genus according to Paramonov, 1964 *1040*

A—*multipapillatum, Bunonema*
1. Place asterisk before *Bunonema*
2. Add: *valid name according to Goodey, 1963 *881*

A—*multipapillatus, Dorylaimellus*
Add: NOTE: placed in *species inquirendae* by Heyns, 1964 *906*

A,C,T—*multipapillatus, Longidorus*
1. Change species name to *multipapillata*
2. Transpose entire entry to immediately below *multidentatus, Panagrolaimoides*
3. Add: *Longidorella* (Schuurmans Stekhoven & Teunissen, 1938) Siddiqi, 1962 *1080*
NOTE: placed in *species inquirendae* by Hooper, 1961 *909*

A—*multipara, Rhabditella*
Add: *881* = *Pelodera axei* Cobbold, 1889

PAGE 95

A—*multisetosa*, var. *hallensis, Monhystera*
Add: *1028* = *Monhystera hallensis* Meyl, 1961

A,C—*multitubiferus, Plectus*
1. Change species name to *multitubiferum*
2. Add: *Chronogaster* (Imamura, 1931) Maggenti, 1961 *1020*
Paraplectonema (Imamura, 1931) Loof & Jairajpuri, 1965 *1002*

N—*mulveyi*
Aporcelaimus Brzeski, 1962 *794*

N—*mulveyi*
Hexatylus Das, 1964 *844*

A—*murisieri, Trilobus*
Add: NOTE: placed in *species inquirendae* by Andrássy, 1964 *777*

51

A—murithi, Longidorella
Add: *Nordia* (Altherr, 1950) Jairajpuri
& Siddiqi, 1964 *950*
Enchodorella (Altherr, 1950) Sid-
diqi, 1964 *1090a*

N—musae
Mauginia Penso, 1939 *1040a*

N—musae
Mesodorylaimus Geraert, 1962 *865*

A—muscorum, Oncholaimus
Add: *815* syn: *Mononchus bastiani* de
Man, 1876
995 syn: *Mononchus papillatus* of
de Man, 1880 & 1884

A—musicola, Tylenchus
Add: *993 Tylenchorhynchus musicola*
of Filipjev & Schuurmans Stekhoven,
1941 = *Pratylenchus goodeyi* Sher
& Allen, 1953
993 Anguillulina musicola of Goodey,
1932 = *Pratylenchus goodeyi* Sher
& Allen, 1953

N—musicolus
Paraseinura Timm, 1960 *1134*

N—mustafi
Enchodorella Husain & Khan, 1965
916

A,C—mutabile, Criconemoides
1. Change species name to *mutabilis*
2. Add: *881 Criconemoides mutabile*
of Raski, 1952 = *Criconemoides
raskii* Goodey, 1963
Nothocriconema (Taylor, 1936) de
Grisse & Loof, 1965 *891*
891 syn: *Criconemoides raskii*
Goodey, 1963
891 syn: *Criconemoides magnoliae*
Edward & Misra, 1964

PAGE 96

A—mycogenes, Aphelenchus
Add: NOTE: placed in *species inquirendae* by Goodey, 1960 *876*

C—mycophilus, Procephalobus
Delete asterisks and footnote

N—naasi
Meloidogyne Franklin, 1965 *861*

N—nagini
Seinura Husain & Khan, 1965 *918*

N—nainianus
Paratylenchus Edward & Misra, 1963
849

N—nainitalensis
Criconemoides Edward & Misra, 1963
848
Macroposthonia (Edward & Misra,
1963) de Grisse & Loof, 1965 *891*

A,C—nannus, Helicotylenchus
1. Delete asterisks and footnote
2. Add: *1065* = *Tylenchus dihystera*
Cobb, 1893

A,C—nanus, Cephalobus
1. Delete footnote
2. Add: *Cephalobus* [*Cephalobus*] de
Man, 1880 *786*
*valid name according to Meyl,
1961 *1028*

N—nanus
Ditylenchus Siddiqi, 1963 *1082*

A—nanus, Paratylenchus
Add: *809* syn: *Paratylenchus amblycephalus* Reuver, 1959
857 syn: *Paratylenchus projectus*
Jenkins, 1956
866 = *Paratylenchus bukowinensis*
Micoletzky, 1922

N—natator
Macrolaimus Timm, 1960 *1133a*

A—naticochensis, Aphelenchus
Add: NOTE: placed in *species inquirendae* by Goodey, 1960 *876*

A—naticochensis, Plectus
Add: *1020* = *Plectus parietinus* Bastian, 1865

A—neglectus, Aphelenchus
Add: *993* syn: *Pratylenchus minyus*
Sher & Allen, 1953

N—neoaberrans
Tylenchus [Filenchus] Goodey, 1963
881
881 syn: Psilenchus aberrans
Thorne, 1949

N—neoamblycephalus
Paratylenchus Geraert, 1965 866
866 syn: Paratylenchus amblycephalus
Reuver, 1959 (in part)

N—neoaxestus
Criconemoides Jairajpuri & Siddiqi,
1963 948
Macroposthonia (Jairajpuri & Siddiqi,
1963) de Grisse & Loof, 1965 891

N—neocephalatus
Acrobeles Kannan, 1961 958

N—neoformis
Helicotylenchus Siddiqi & Husain,
1964 1105

N—neoformis
Psilenchus Jairajpuri & Siddiqi, 1963
947

N—neogracilis
Tylenchus [Filenchus] Goodey, 1963
881
881 syn: Psilenchus gracilis Thorne,
1949

PAGE 97

N—neortha
Belondira Siddiqi, 1964 1089

N—neotumbridgensis
Mononchus [Mononchus] Kannan, 1961
959

N—nepalensis
Belondira Siddiqi, 1964 1089

N—newmexicana
Bunonema Massey, 1964 1025a

A,C—nicotiana, Tetylenchus
1. Change the two lines under species
name to: Tetylenchus Yokoo &
Tanaka in Tanaka & Tsumagori,
1954 676b (c)

2. Add: NOTE: believed to be a
Rotylenchulus by Baker, 1962 784
& Merny, 1964 1027

N—nigeriense
Xiphinema Luc, 1961 1010

N—nigeriensis
Aphasmatylenchus Sher, 1965 1069

N—nigeriensis
Dolichodorus Luc & Caveness, 1963
1012

N—nigeriensis
Peltamigratus Sher, 1964 1068

A—nikkoensis, Tylencholaimus
Add: NOTE: placed in species inquirendae by Jairajpuri, 1965 945

N—nirulai
Longidorus Siddiqi, 1965 1097

N—nitidum
Axonchium Jairajpuri, 1964 936

A—nivalis, Dorylaimus
Add: NOTE: placed in species inquirendae by Meyl, 1961 1028

N—noctiscriptus
Psilenchus Andrássy, 1962 769a

A,C—nodicaudatus, Prismatolaimus
1. Delete parentheses from first line
under species name
2. Add: 577 syn: Mononchulus ventralis Cobb, 1918

C—nodifera, Diploscapter
Change species name to nodifer

N—nortoni
Belonolaimus Rau, 1963 1046

PAGE 98

A—novaezealandiae, Dorylaimus
Add: Mesodorylaimus (Cobb, 1904)
Goodey, 1963 881

N—novus
Oxydirus Jairajpuri, 1965 944

53

N—nudata
Hemicycliophora Colbran, 1963 832

A—nudicapitatus, Diplogaster
Add: Acrostichus   (Steiner,   1914)
Massey, 1962 1024

N—nudum
Doryllium Thorne, 1964 1133

A—nudum, Litonema
Add: NOTE: placed in species inquirendae by Goodey, 1963 881

A—nuesslini, Aphelenchoides
Add: Bursaphelenchus (Rühm, 1956)
Goodey, 1960 876

N—nygellurus
Dorylaimellus Loof, 1964 1001

N—nyongi
Dorylaimus Altherr, 1960 753

A—oahuënsis, Aphelenchoides
Add: Seinura   (Christie,   1939)
Goodey, 1960 876

A—obliquus, Mononchus
Add: NOTE: placed in species inquirendae by Meyl, 1961 1028, but regarded as valid species by Mulvey,
1961 1030

A—obscuricola, Diplogaster
Add: NOTE: placed in species inquirendae by Meyl, 1961 1028

A—obscuridens, Diplogaster
Add: Mononchoides   (Schuurmans
Stekhoven, 1951) Goodey, 1963 881

A—obscurus, Dorylaimus
1. Place asterisk before Eudorylaimus
2. Add: Aporcelaimus (Thorne &
Swanger, 1936) Goodey, 1961 877
*regarded as valid genus by Loof,
1964 1001

N—obscurus
Tylencholaimus Jairajpuri, 1965 945

N—obscurus
Tylenchulus Colbran, 1961 830a

N—obtusicaudatum
Criconemoides Heyns, 1962 901
891 = Criconemoides   ferniae   Luc,
1959

A—obtusicaudatum, Triplonchium
Add: NOTE: placed in species inquirendae by Goodey, 1963 881

A—obtusicaudatus, Dorylaimus
Add: 995 Dorylaimus obtusicaudatus
(male form I) of de Man, 1880 and
Dorylaimus obtusicaudatus (male)
of   de   Man,   1884 = Dorylaimus
parabastiani Paetzold, 1958
NOTE: According to Loof, 1961 995,
Dorylaimus obtusicaudatus (male
form II) of de Man, 1880 is species inquirendae.

A—obtusicaudatus, Enoplochilus
Add: Oionchus (Kreis, 1932) Andrássy, 1961 766a

A,C—obtusicaudatus, Plectus
1. Delete asterisks and footnote
2. Add: 881 syn: Acrobeles [Acro-
beloides] minor Thorne, 1925
Acrobeloides   (Daday,   1899)
Goodey, 1963 881

N—obtusicaudatus
Tylenchus Erzhanov, 1964 852a

A—obtusicaudus, Iotonchium
Add: NOTE: placed in species inquirendae by Meyl, 1961 1028

A—obtusum, Xiphinema
Add: NOTE: placed in species inquirendae by Luc & Tarjan, 1963 1019

N—obtusus
Ektaphelenchus Massey, 1956 1023

N—obtusus
*Hemicriconemoides   Colbran,   1962
831 (c)

Criconemoides (Colbran, 1962) Siddiqi & Goodey, 1963 *1103*
*valid genus according to de Grisse & Loof, 1965 *891*

A—*obtusus, Mononchus*
Add: NOTE: placed in *species inquirendae* by Clark, 1960 *815*

A—*obtusus, Trichodorus*
1. Place asterisk before *Trichodorus*
2. Add: *valid species according to Seinhorst, 1963 *1063*

A—*obtusus, Tylenchus*
Add: NOTE: (2) placed in *species inquirendae* by Goodey, 1963 *881*

A—*occidentalis, Diplogaster*
1. Place asterisk before *Diplogasteritus*
2. Add: *Acrostichus* (Steiner, 1932) Massey, 1962 *1024*
*valid genus according to Goodey, 1963 *881*

N—*ockerti*
Cobbonchus Coetzee, 1965 *829*

N—*octopapillata*
Bastiana Meyl, 1961 *1028*
1028 syn: *Bastiana gracilis,* var. *octopapillata* Meyl, 1954

A—*okai, Butlerius*
1. Place asterisk before *Butlerius*
2. Add: *valid genus according to Goodey, 1963 *881*

N—*okhlaensis*
Nordia Jairajpuri & Siddiqi, 1964 *950*
Enchodorella (Jairajpuri & Siddiqi, 1964) Siddiqi, 1964 *1090a*

A,C—*olaae, Tylenchus*
1. Delete Note
2. Add: *1065* = *Tylenchus dihystera* Cobb, 1893

A—*oliveirae, Aphelenchoides*
Add: *Seinura* (Christie, 1939) Goodey, 1960 *876*

A,C—*onoense, Criconemoides*
1. Change species name to *onoensis*
2. Add: *Macroposthonia* (Luc, 1959) de Grisse & Loof, 1965 *891*

N—*oostenbrinki*
Criconemoides Loof, 1964 *1001*
Macroposthonia (Loof, 1964) de Grisse & Loof, 1965 *891*
Neocriconema (Loof, 1964) Diab & Jenkins, 1965 *845*
Mesocriconema (Loof, 1964) Andrássy, 1965 *781b*

N—*oostenbrinki*
Oostenbrinkella Jairajpuri, 1965 *940*

N—*operosa*
Pelodera [*Pelodera*] Andrássy, 1962 *769a*

N—*ophiocercus*
Iotonchus Clark, 1961 *816*

A—*opisthocirculus, Plectus*
Add: *1020* = *Plectus parvus* Bastian, 1865

N—*opisthohysterum*
Xiphinema Siddiqi, 1961 *1076*

N—*orbum*
Xiphinema Siddiqi, 1964 *1093*

A—*orbus, Tylenchus*
1. Place asterisk before *Tylenchus* [*Filenchus*]
2. Add: *Filenchus* (Andrássy, 1954) Meyl, 1961 *1028*
*valid name according to Goodey, 1963 *881*

N—*orientalis*
Diploscapter Kannan, 1960 *955*

N—*orientalis*
Rotylenchus Siddiqi & Husain, 1964 *1105*

A—*ormerodis, Aphelenchus*
Add: NOTE: placed in *species inquirendae* by Goodey, 1960 *876*

A—*ornata, Rhabditis*
Add: NOTE: (2) placed in *species inquirendae* by Meyl, 1961 *1028*

A,C,T—*ornatum, Criconemoides*
1. Change species name to *ornata*
2. Transpose entire entry to immediately after *ormerodis*, var. *longicollis, Aphelenchus*
3. Add: *Macroposthonia* (Raski, 1958) de Grisse & Loof, 1965 *891*

N—*ornatus*
Diphtherophora Erzhanov, 1964 *852a*

A—*ornatus, Plectus*
Add: NOTE: placed in *species inquirendae* by Meyl, 1961 *1028*

N—*orthodon*
Drepanodorus Loof, 1964 *1001*

A—*ortus, Anguillulina*
Add: *Neoditylenchus* (Fuchs, 1938) Meyl, 1961 *1028*

N—*oryzae*
Heterodera Luc & Berdon Brizuela, 1961 *1011*

N—*oryzae*
Lenonchium Siddiqi, 1965 *1098*

A,C—*oryzae, Tylenchus*
1. Delete Note
2. Add: *Hirschmannia* (van Breda de Haan, 1902) Luc & Goodey, 1962 *1014*
1014 syn: *Radopholus gigas* Andrássy, 1954
1014 syn: *Radopholus mucronatus* Das, 1960
Hirschmanniella (van Breda de Haan, 1902) Luc & Goodey, 1964 *1015*

PAGE 105

A—*oswegoensis, Aphelenchoides*
Add: *Seinura* (van der Linde, 1938) Goodey, 1960 *876*

A—*ottoi, Pristionchus*
Add: *881* = *Diplogaster lheritieri* Maupas, 1919

N—*ovalis*
Meloidogyne Riffle, 1963 *1049*

N—*ovata*
Hemicycliophora Colbran, 1962 *831*

N—*oxiana*
Heterodera Kirjanova, 1962 *983*

A,C—*oxurus, Aphelenchoides*
1. Change species name to *oxura*
2. Add: *Seinura* (Paesler, 1957) Goodey, 1960 *876*

A—*oxycephalus, Aulolaimus*
Add: *995 Aulolaimus oxycephalus* of Meyl, 1954 = *Aulolaimus meyli* Loof, 1961

A—*oxyuris, Cephalobus*
Add: *Panagrolaimus* (Bütschli, 1873) Goodey, 1963 *881*

PAGE 106

A,C—*pachtaicus, Longidorus*
1. Change species name to *pachtaicum*
2. Add: *Xiphinema* (Tulaganov, 1938) Kirjanova, 1951 *342*
NOTE: placed in *species inquirendae* by Luc & Tarjan, 1963 *1019*

A—*pachylaimus, Procephalobus*
Add: *Panagrolaimus* (Schuurmans Stekhoven & Teunissen, 1938) Goodey, 1963 *881*

N—*pachyurus*
Peltamigratus Loof, 1964 *1001*

N—*pacificus*
Criconemoides Andrássy, 1965 *781b*

A—*paesleri, Diplogaster* Gunhold
Add: *Koerneria* (Gunhold, 1952) Meyl, 1961 *1028*

N—*paesleri*
Eudorylaimus Andrássy, 1964 *775*

N—*paetzoldi*
Mesodorylaimus Altherr, 1965 *757a*

N—*paetzoldi*
Panagrolaimus Goodey, 1963 *881*
881 syn: *Neocephalobus halophilus* of Paetzold, 1958

N—*pakistanensis*
Dorylaimoides Siddiqi, 1964 *1093*

N—*pakistanensis*
Trichodorus Siddiqi, 1962 *1081*

N—*pakistanensis*
Tylencholaimus Timm, 1964 *1140*

N—*pakistanicum*
Discolaimium Timm & Bhuiyan, 1963 *1143*
938a = *Axonchium amplicolle* Cobb, 1920

A—*palliati, Fuchsia*
Add: *Mikoletzkya* (Rühm, 1956) Baker, 1962 *784*

N—*palmaris*
Phytorhabditis Lordello & de Oliveira, 1963 *1005*

N—*palmatum*
Criconema Siddiqi & Southey, 1962 *1111*

N—*palustris*
Falcihasta Clark, 1964 *828*

A—*palustris, Plectus*
Add: *Proteroplectus* (de Man, 1880) Paramonov, 1964 *1040*
798 syn: *Plectus tenuis* of Chodorowska, 1959 and 1961 & of Kozlowska, 1962 in part
NOTE: placed in *species inquirendae* by Meyl, 1961 *1028*

A—*palustris, Urolabes*
Add: NOTE: placed in *species inquirendae* by Meyl, 1961 *1028*

A—*palustris crassicauda, Teratocephalus*
Add: *Euteratocephalus* (Kischke, 1956) Meyl, 1961 *1028*

N—*panaxi*
Aphelenchoides Skarbilovich & Potekhina, 1959 *1114*

A—*panurgus, Ditylenchus*
Add: *Neoditylenchus* (Rühm, 1956) Meyl, 1961 *1028*

A,C—*papillata, Tripyla*
1. Delete asterisks and footnote
2. Place asterisk before *593*
3. Add: *valid synonymy according to Brzeski, 1964 *806*

A—*papillata, var. cornuta, Tripyla*
Add: *806*? *Tripyla papillata*, var. *cornuta* of Andrássy, 1952 = *Tripyla glomerans* Bastian, 1865

A—*papillata, var. crystallifera, Tripyla*
Add: *806* = *Tripyla glomerans* Bastian, 1865

A—*papillatus, Actinolaimus*
Add: *781 Actinolaimus papillatus* of Altherr, 1960 = *Actinolaimus gracillima* Andrássy, 1964
Actinca (Schneider, 1935) Andrássy, 1964 *781*

A—*papillatus, Aphanolaimus*
Add: NOTE: (2) Andrássy, 1961 *766* suggests that this species appears to be an *Ironus*

N—*papillatus*
Calolaimus Timm, 1964 *1140*

A—*papillatus, Diastolaimus*
Add: *Chambersiella* (Rahm, 1928) Sanwal, 1960 *1059*

A—*papillatus, Dorylaimus*
Add: NOTE: placed in *species inquirendae* by Meyl, 1961 *1028*

A—*papillatus, Mononchus*
Add: *995 Mononchus papillatus* of de Man, 1880 & 1884 = *Oncholaimus muscorum* Dujardin, 1845

N—*par*
Pelodera [*Coarctadera*] Andrássy, 1962 *769a*

paraagilis

parasitica

A—paraagilis, Dorylaimus
1. Place asterisk before Dorylaimus
2. Add: *valid genus according to Goodey, 1963 881

A—parabastiani, Dorylaimus
Add: 995 syn: Dorylaimus obtusicaudatus (male form I) of de Man, 1880 and Dorylaimus obtusicaudatus (male) of de Man, 1884

N—paracirculifer
Eudorylaimus Brzeski, 1962 796

N—paraclava
Belondira Jairajpuri, 1964 936

A—paracommunis, Plectus
Add: 1020 = Plectus parvus Bastian, 1865

N—paraconura
Discolaimium Siddiqi, 1965 1096

N—paraconurus
Dorylaimoides Heyns, 1963 904

N—paradetritophagus
Panagrolaimus Goodey, 1963 881
881 syn: Panagrolaimus detritophagus of Rühm, 1956

N—paradoxum
Thornenema Siddiqi, 1965 1098a

C,T—paraelongata, Monhystera
1. Change species name to pareleganttula
2. Transpose entire entry to page 110, immediately after parazschokkei, Mononchus

PAGE 109

A—paraelongata, Rhabditis
Add: NOTE: placed in species inquirendae by Meyl, 1961 1028

A—paraelongatum, Xiphinema
Add: 1019 = Dorylaimus [Longidorus] diversicaudatum Micoletzky, 1927

N—paragracillima
Monhystera Goodey, 1963 881
881 syn: Monhystera gracillima of de Man, 1921

A—paragricola, Tylenchus
Add: Aglenchus (Paetzold, 1958) Meyl, 1961 1028
Tylenchus [Aglenchus] Paetzold, 1958 881
772 = Tylenchus agricola de Man, 1884

A—paraguayensis, Plectus
Add: NOTE: placed in species inquirendae by Maggenti, 1961 1020

N—paralongicaudata
Caloosia Siddiqi & Goodey, 1964 1103
1103 syn: Hemicycliophora longicauda of Siddiqi, 1961

A—paralongicaudatus, Cephalobus
Add: NOTE: placed in species inquirendae by Meyl, 1961 1028

N—paramaximus
Paralongidorus Heyns, 1965 908a

A—paramicrostoma, Diplogaster
Add: NOTE: placed in species inquirendae by Meyl, 1961 1028

A—pararmatus, Diplogaster
Add: NOTE: placed in species inquirendae by Goodey, 1963 881

A,C—pararobustus, Tylenchorhynchus
1. Add: Hoplolaimus (Schuurmans Stekhoven & Teunissen, 1938) Sher, 1963 1066
1066 syn: Hoplolaimus proporicus Goodey, 1957
1066 syn: Hoplolaimus angustalatus Whitehead, 1959
1066 syn: Hoplolaimus kittenbergeri Andrássy, 1961
2. Change note to: placed in species inquirendae by Sher, 1961 1065

N—parasaprophilus
Aphelenchoides Sanwal, 1965 1061a

A—parasetariae, Xiphinema
Add: NOTE: placed in species inquirendae by Luc & Tarjan, 1963 1019

N—parasitica
Monhystera Penso, 1938 530

58

paratenuicaudata

N—*paratenuicaudata*
Seinura Geraert, 1962 *864*

N—*parateres*
Dorylaimoides Siddiqi, 1964 *1093*

N—*paratrifolii*
Heterodera Kirjanova, 1963 *984*

A,C—*parietinus, Plectus*
1. Delete asterisks and footnote
2. Add *1020* syn: *Plectus fusiformis* Bastian, 1865
1020 syn: *Plectus velox* Bastian, 1865
1020 syn: *Plectus patagonicus* de Man, 1904
1020 syn: *Plectus hawaiiensis* Cobb, 1906
1020 syn: *Plectus antarcticus* de Man, 1904
1020 syn: *Plectus naticochensis* Steiner, 1920
1020 syn: *Plectus pusteri* Fuchs, 1930
1020 syn: *Plectus intermedius* Cobb, 1893

A—*parietinus*, var. *sinensis, Aphelenchus*
Add: *761* = *Aphelenchoides sinensis* Andrássy, 1960

N—*parva*
Belondira Thorne, 1964 *1133*

N—*parva*
Diphtherophora Siddiqi, 1964 *1092a*

A—*parva, Longidorella*
Add: *961 Longidorella purva* of Tarjan, 1953 = *Enchodorella americanum* Khan, 1964

N—*parvula*
Criconemoides Siddiqi, 1961 *1077*
Criconemella (Siddiqi, 1961) de Grisse & Loof, 1965 *891*

parvus

A,C,T—*parvum, Criconemoides*
1. Change species name to *parva*
2. Transpose entire entry to immediately after *parva, Belondira*
3. Add: *Criconemella* (Raski, 1952) de Grisse & Loof, 1965 *891*

A—*parvum, Labronema*
Add: *Thornenema* (Williams, 1959) Williams, 1964 *1150*

A—*parvum, Micronema*
1. Place asterisk before *Micronema*
2. Add: *valid species according to Meyl, 1961 *1028*

A—*parvus, Aporcelaimus*
Add: *1028* = *Dorylaimus superbus* de Man, 1880

A—*parvus, Diplogaster*
Add: NOTE: placed in *species inquirendae* by Goodey, 1963 *881*

N—*parvus*
Dorylaimellus Jairajpuri, 1965 *942*

N—*parvus*
Helicotylenchus Williams, 1960 *1147*
Rotylenchulus (Williams, 1960) Sher, 1961 *1065*
881 = *Rotylenchulus reniformis* Linford & Oliveira, 1940

A—*parvus, Plectus*
Add: *1020* syn: *Plectus belgicae* de Man, 1904
1020 syn: *Plectus communis* Bütschli, 1873 in part
1020 syn: *Plectus paracommunis* Hoeppli, 1926
1020 syn: *Plectus potamogeti* Schneider, 1937
1020 syn: *Plectus opisthocercus* Andrássy, 1958
Proteroplectus (Bastian, 1865) Paramonov, 1964 *1040*

N—*parvus*
Prismatolaimus Milne, 1963 *1029*

N—*parvus*
Tylenchus [*Aglenchus*] Siddiqi, 1963
1083

N—*parvus*
Tyleptus Jairajpuri, 1965 *944*

A,C—*patagonicus, Plectus*
1. Delete asterisks and footnote
2. Add: *1020* = *Plectus parietinus* Bastian, 1865

A—*paucus, Tylenchorhynchus*
Add: NOTE: placed in *species inquirendae* by Meyl, 1961 *1028*

N—*pauli*
Iotonchus Heyns & Lagerwey, 1965 *908c*

N—*paulistanum*
Xiphinema Carvalho, 1965 *813*

A—*paulyi, Diplogaster*
Add: *881* = *Diplogaster agilis* Skwarra, 1921

A—*pavlovskii, Dorylaimus*
Add: *Eudorylaimus* (Tulaganov, 1949) Goodey, 1963 *881*

A—*paxi, Iota*
Add: NOTE: placed in *species inquirendae* by Siddiqi & Goodey, 1964 *1103*

N—*paxilli*
Helicotylenchus Yuen, 1964 *1162*

N—*pectinatum*
Criconema Colbran, 1962 *831*

PAGE 114

A,C—*pellucida, Trischistoma*
1. Change species name to *pellucidum*
2. Place asterisk before *Trischistoma*
3. Add: *valid genus according to Brzeski, 1965 *807*

A—*penardi, Aphelenchus*
1. Place asterisk before *Aphelenchoides*
2. Add: *valid genus according to Meyl, 1961 *1028*

A—*penardi, Bunonema*
1. Place asterisk before *Bunonema*
2. Add: *valid name according to Goodey, 1963 *881*

N—*penetrans*
Belonenchus Thorne, 1964 *1133*

A—*penetrans, Dorylaimus*
Add: *Longidorella* (Thorne & Swanger, 1936) Goodey, 1963 *881*
Nordia (Thorne & Swanger, 1936) Jairajpuri & Siddiqi, 1964 *950*
Enchodorella (Thorne & Swanger, 1936) Siddiqi, 1964 *1090a*

A—*penetrans, Tylenchus*
Add: *993* syn: *Tylenchus gulosus* Kühn, 1890
993 syn: *Tylenchus pratensis* of Steiner, 1927; Bovien, 1927; & Steiner, 1932
993 syn: *Anguillulina pratensis* of Goodey, 1932 & 1933; & Schneider, 1939
993 syn: *Pratylenchus pratensis* of Filipjev & Schuurmans Stekhoven, 1941; & Goodey, 1951
761 syn: *Dolichodorus heterocercus* Kreis, 1930
NOTE: Loof, 1961 *996* proposes that *Tylenchus penetrans* be placed on the Specific List of Official Names in Zoology, even though it is antedated by *Tylenchus gulosus* Kühn, 1890.

N—*peperpotti*
Gracilacus Schoemaker, 1963 *1062*
Paratylenchus (Schoemaker, 1963) Siddiqi & Goodey, 1964 *1103*

N—*peraticus*
Gracilacus Raski, 1962 *1044*
Paratylenchus (Raski, 1962) Siddiqi & Goodey, 1964 *1103*

N—*percivali*
Iotonchus Clark, 1961 *816*
826 syn: *Mononchus* [*Iotonchus*] *trichurus* of Allgén, 1929
826 syn: *Iotonchus trichurus* of Mulvey, 1963 (in part)

60

A—*perplexa, Belondira*
Add: NOTE: not a *Belondira* according
to Jairajpuri, 1964 *936*

PAGE 115

A,C—*peruensis, Iota*
1. Delete asterisks and footnote
2. Add: *Macroposthonia* (Cobb, 1924)
de Grisse & Loof, 1965 *891*
781b syn: *Criconema congolense*
Schuurmans Stekhoven and Teunissen, 1938

A—*peruënsis, Neocephalobus*
Add: *Panagrolaimus* (Steiner & Christie, 1939) Goodey, 1963 *881*

N—*perveeni*
Enchodorella Khan, 1964 *961*

A—*pestis, Cacopaurus*
1. Place asterisk before *Cacopaurus*
2. Add: *Paratylenchus* (Thorne, 1943)
Goodey, 1963 *881*
*valid genus according to Siddiqi &
Goodey, 1964 *1103*

N—*petasus*
Criconemoides Wu, 1965 *1160*
Nothocriconema (Wu, 1965) de
Grisse & Loof, 1965 *891*

A—*petithi, Anguillonema*
Add: *Neoditylenchus* (Fuchs, 1938)
Meyl, 1961 *1028*

A—*phloxidis, Ditylenchus*
Add: *881* = *Anguillula dipsaci* Kühn,
1857
NOTE: placed in *species inquirendae*
by Meyl, 1961 *1028*

PAGE 116

N—*phoxodorus*
Aulolaimoides Andrássy, 1964 *779*

A,C—*phyllobius, Anguillulina*
1. Change species name to *phyllobia*
2. Add: *Nothanguina* (Thorne, 1934)
Thorne, 1961 *1132*

N—*picardi*
Dorylaimus Altherr, 1963 *755*

A—*picei, Panagrolaimus*
Add: NOTE: placed in *species inquirendae* by Meyl, 1961 *1028*

A—*picei, Rhabditolaimus*
Add: *Neodiplogasteroides* (Fuchs,
1931) Meyl, 1961 *1028*
Dirhabdilaimus (Fuchs, 1931)
Baker, 1962 *784*
NOTE: placed in *species inquirendae*
by Meyl, 1961 *1028*

A—*picicola, Diplogasteroides*
Add: *Diplogasteroides* (Rühm, 1956)
Meyl, 1961 *1028*
Rhabditolaimus (Rühm, 1956)
Goodey, 1963 *881*

N—*pileatum*
Triplonchium Andrássy, 1961 *765*

A—*pillulifer, Tylenchus*
Add: NOTE: placed in *species incertae
sedis* by Loof, 1961 *995*

N—*pini*
Basirotyleptus Siddiqi & Khan, 1965
1109

N—*pini*
Parasitorhabditis Lazarevskaja, 1961
990a

A—*pini, Stictylus*
Add: *Sphaerulariopsis* (Fuchs, 1929)
Nickle, 1963 *1036*

N—*pini*
Xiphinema Heyns, 1965 *908*

A—*pinicola, Diplogaster*
Add: *Mikoletzkya* (Thorne, 1935)
Baker, 1962 *784*

A—*piniperdae, Bursaphelenchus*
1. Place asterisk before *Bursaphelenchus*
2. Add: *valid genus according to
Meyl, 1961 *1028*

N—*piniperdae*
Ektaphelenchus Kakulija & Lazarevskaja, 1965 *954a*

piniperdae

A—*piniperdae, Panagrolaimus*
1. Place asterisk before *Panagrolaimus*
2. Add: *valid species according to
Goodey, 1963 *881*

N—*piniphili*
Neodiplogaster Rühm, 1956 *881*
881 syn: *Neodiplogaster pissodis piniphili* Rühm, 1956
881 syn: *Tylenchodon pissodis,* var.
piniphili Fuchs, 1938

A—*piniphili, Stictylus*
Add: *Sphaerulariopsis* (Fuchs, 1929)
Nickle, 1963 *1036*

A—*pinophilus, Anguillulina*
Add: *Neoditylenchus* (Thorne, 1935)
Goodey, 1963 *881*

PAGE 117

A—*piracicabensis, Odontopharynx*
Add: *Mononchoides* (Rahm, 1928)
Goodey, 1963 *881*

N—*piracicaboides*
Mononchus [*Iotonchus*] Carvalho, 1960
811b
Iotonchus Heyns & Lagerwey, 1965
908c

A—*pissodis, Tylenchodon*
1. Place asterisk before *Neodiplogaster*
2. Add: *881* syn: *Neodiplogaster
pissodis pissodis* (Fuchs, 1930)
Goodey, 1951
*valid name according to Goodey,
1963 *881*

A—*pissodis notati, Parasitaphelenchus*
Add: NOTE: placed in *species inquirendae* by Goodey, 1960 *876*

A—*pissodis piceae, Parasitaphelenchus*
Add: NOTE: placed in *species inquirendae* by Goodey, 1960 *876*

A—*pissodis piniphili, Neodiplogaster*
Add: *881* = *Neodiplogaster piniphili*
Rühm, 1956

A—*pissodis pissodis, Neodiplogaster*
Add: *881* = *Tylenchodon pissodis*
Fuchs, 1930

polonicus

A—*pissodis,* var. *piniphili, Tylenchodon*
Add: *881* = *Neodiplogaster piniphili*
Rühm, 1956

A—*pityokteinophilus, Ditylenchus*
Add: *Neoditylenchus* (Rühm, 1956)
Meyl, 1961 *1028*

N—*pizai*
Mesodorylaimus Lordello, 1965 *1004a*

A—*planipedius, Dorylaimus*
Add: †*Eudorylaimus* (Merzheevskaya,
1951) Andrássy, 1959 *50d*

N—*plumariae*
Helicotylenchus Khan & Basir, 1964
977

N—*pluvialis*
Prodontorhabditis Timm, 1961 *1137*

N—*pluvialis*
Tylencholaimellus Siddiqi, 1965 *1098*

N—*poghossianae*
Meloidogyne Kirjanova, 1963 *984*
984 syn: *Meloidogyne acronea* of
Poghossian, 1961

A—*poligraphi, Bursaphelenchus*
1. Place asterisk before *Bursaphelenchus*
2. Add: *valid genus according to
Goodey, 1960 *876*

PAGE 118

A—*poligraphi, Rhodolaimus*
1. Place asterisk before *Rhodolaimus*
2. Add: *valid name according to
Goodey, 1963 *881*

N—*polonicum*
Witoldinema Brzeski, 1961 *789*

A—*polonicus, Mononchus*
Add: NOTE: placed in *species inquirendae* by Mulvey, 1961 *1030*

N—*polonicus*
Tylencholaimellus Szczygiel, 1962
1122

polyblastus

A—*polyblastus, Dorylaimus*
Add: *Mesodorylaimus* (Bastian, 1865) Goodey, 1963 *881*

A,C—*polyhypnus, Tylenchus*
1. Delete asterisks and footnote
2. Place asterisk before *Tylenchus* [*Filenchus*]
3. Add: *Filenchus* (Steiner & Albin, 1946) Meyl, 1961 *1028*
 *valid name according to Goodey, 1963 *881*

N—*ponderosa*
Acrostichus Massey, 1962 *1024*
Filipjevella (Massey, 1962) Lazarevskaja, 1965 *990c*

N—*porifer*
Dorylaimoides Loof, 1964 *1001*

N—*porosum*
Poronema Heyns, 1963 *903*
Lordellonema (Heyns, 1963) Heyns, 1963 *903*

A—*porosus, Trichodorus*
Add: *1081* syn: *Trichodorus bucrius* Lordello & Zamith, 1958

N—*porta*
Belondira Thorne, 1964 *1133*

A—*potamogeti, Plectus*
Add: *1020* = *Plectus parvus* Bastian, 1865

N—*potus*
Mesodorylaimus Heyns, 1963 *904*

N—*pounamua*
Cobbonchus Clark, 1961 *817*

A—*pratense, Xiphinema*
Add: *1019* = *Xiphinema elongatum* Schuurmans Stekhoven & Teunissen, 1938

A—*pratensis, Tylenchus*
Add: *993 Pratylenchus pratensis* of Paetzold, 1955 = *Pratylenchus irregularis* Loof, 1960
993 Anguillulina pratensis of Goffart, 1929 in part = *Pratylenchus crenatus* Loof, 1960 (*c*)

primitivus

993 Pratylenchus pratensis of Thorne, 1949; Sher & Allen, 1953; Oostenbrink, 1954; & Coomans, 1958 in part = *Pratylenchus crenatus* Loof, 1960

993 Pratylenchus pratensis of Yokoo, 1956 = *Tylenchus coffeae* Zimmermann, 1898

993 Tylenchus pratensis of Steiner, 1927; Bovien, 1927; & Steiner, 1932 = *Tylenchus penetrans* Cobb, 1917

993 Anguillulina pratensis of Goodey, 1932 & 1933; & Schneider, 1939 = *Tylenchus penetrans*, Cobb, 1917

993 Pratylenchus pratensis of Filipjev & Schuurmans Stekhoven, 1941; & Goodey, 1951 = *Tylenchus penetrans* Cobb, 1917

993 Pratylenchus pratensis of Slootweg, 1956 = *Pratylenchus convallariae* Seinhorst, 1959

A—*pratensis,* var. *bicaudatus, Pratylenchus*
Add: *1028* = *Pratylenchus bicaudatus* Meyl, 1961
NOTE: placed in *species inquirendae* by Loof, 1960 *993*

A—*pratensis,* var. *tenuistriatus, Pratylenchus*
Add: NOTE: placed in *species inquirendae* by Loof, 1960 *993*

N—*pravamphidia*
Basiria Andrássy, 1963 *774*

N—*prelli*
Filenchus Rühm, 1965 *1055c*

N—*pretoriensis*
Dorylaimoides Heyns, 1963 *904*

A—*primitivus, Alaimus*
Add: *1028* syn: *Alaimus mucronatus* Altherr, 1950

A—*primitivus, Dorylaimus*
1. Place asterisk before *484*
2. Add: *incorrect synonymy according to Seinhorst, 1963 *1063*

N—*princeps*
Criconemoides Andrássy, 1962 *769a*
Nothocriconema (Andrássy, 1962) de
Grisse & Loof, 1965 *891*

N—*proamphidum*
Kochinema Heyns, 1963 *904*

A—*procera, Alloionema*
Add: *881 Anguilluloides procera* of
Rühm, 1956 = *Anguilluloides treme-
bunda* Goodey, 1963

A—*prodelphis, Rhabditolaimus*
Add: *Dirhabdilaimus* (Steiner, 1936)
Goodey, 1963 *881*

N—*prodenticulatus*
Mylonchulus Mulvey, 1961 *1030*

N—*profestus*
Eudorylaimus Andrássy, 1963 *774*

A—*profundis, Dorylaimus*
Add: *Mesodorylaimus* (Cobb, 1904)
Goodey, 1963 *881*

N—*profundus*
Dolichodorus Luc, 1960 *1008*

N—*projectus*
Dorylaimellus Heyns, 1962 *898*

A—*projectus, Paratylenchus*
Add: *857* = *Paratylenchus   nanus*
Cobb, 1923

N—*projectus*
Tylencholaimellus Siddiqi, 1964 *1092a*

A—*prolificus, Dorylaimus*
Add: *Mesodorylaimus* (Thorne &
Swanger, 1936) Goodey, 1963 *881*

N—*prominens*
Acrobeles Andrássy, 1964 *779*

N—*propapillatus*
Mononchus Clark, 1960 *814*

A—*propinqua, Tylencholaimus*
Add: *1028* syn: *Thornia regiusi,* var.
magna Paetzold, 1958

N—*propinquus*
Amphidelus Andrássy, 1962 *769*

A—*propinquus, Cephalobus*
Add: *1028* syn: *Acrobeles bonus*
Kirjanova, 1951

A,C—*proporicus, Hopolaimus*
1. Change genus name to *Hoplolaimus*
2. Add: *1066* = *Tylenchorhynchus
pararobustus* Schuurmans Stekhoven
& Teunissen, 1938

A—*proximus, Dorylaimus*
Add: *Mesodorylaimus* (Thorne &
Swanger, 1936) Goodey, 1963 *881*

N—*pruni*
Criconema Siddiqi, 1961 *1077*
Macroposthonia (Siddiqi, 1961) de
Grisse & Loof, 1965 *891*
Mesocriconema (Siddiqi, 1961) An-
drássy, 1965 *781b*

A—*pseudallophysis, Trilobus*
1. Place asterisk before *621*
2. Add: *valid synonymy according to
Andrássy, 1964 *777*

N—*pseudobrachyurum*
Hemicriconemoides de Grisse, 1964
888

A—*pseudoelongata, Rhabditis*
Add: NOTE: placed in *species inquirendae* by Meyl, 1961 *1028*

N—*pseudohercyniensis*
Criconemoides de Grisse & Koen, 1964
890
Macroposthonia (de Grisse & Koen,
1964) de Grisse & Loof, 1965 *891*
Neocriconema (de Grisse & Koen,
1964) Diab & Jenkins, 1965 *845*
Mesocriconema (de Grisse & Koen,
1964) Andrássy, 1964 *781b*

A—*pseudorobustus, Tylenchus*
Add: †*Helicotylenchus* (Steiner, 1914)
Golden, 1956 *254* (*c*)

pseudorostochiensis

NOTE: placed in *species inquirendae* by Tarjan, 1964 *1127*

N—*pseudorostochiensis*
Heterodera Kirjanova, 1963 *984*
984 syn: *Heterodera tabacum* of Kirjanova, 1959

N—*pseudosolivaga*
Criconemoides de Grisse, 1964 *889*
Macroposthonia (de Grisse, 1964) de Grisse & Loof, 1965 *891*
Neocriconema (de Grisse, 1964) Diab & Jenkins, 1965 *845*
Mesocriconema (de Grisse, 1964) Andrássy, 1965 *781b*

A—*pseudostagnalis, Dorylaimus*
Add: *Mesodorylaimus* (Micoletzky, 1927) Goodey, 1963 *881*

N—*pterygatus*
Diplogaster [*Diplogaster*] Timm, 1961 *1136*
Diplogasteritus (Timm, 1961) Timm, 1961 *1136*

A—*pterygiosoma, Rhodolaimus*
1. Place asterisk before *Rhodolaimus*
2. Add: *valid name according to Goodey, 1963 *881*

N—*puellae*
Mesodorylaimus Andrássy, 1963 *774*

N—*puertoricensis*
Hoplolaimus Ramírez, 1964 *1043d*

N—*pulcher*
Eucephalobus Loof, 1964 *1001*

A,C—*pullum, Criconema*
1. Change species name to *pulla*
2. Add: *Macroposthonia* (Kirjanova, 1948) de Grisse & Loof, 1965 *891*

A—*pumilus, Helicotylenchus*
Add: *Rotylenchus* (Perry in Perry, Darling & Thorne, 1959) Sher, 1961 *1065*

N—*pumilus*
Pungentus Andrássy, 1963 *773*

pygmaeus

N—*punctata*
Brevibucca Timm, 1960 *1133a*

A—*punctata, Heterodera*
1. Place asterisk before *Heterodera*
2. Add: *valid name according to Goodey, 1963 *881*

A—*punctata, Rhabditis*
Add: NOTE: placed in *species inquirendae* by Meyl, 1961 *1028*

A—*punctata, Tripyla*
Add: NOTE: placed in *species inquirendae* by Brzeski, 1964 *806*

A—*punctatus, Tobrilus*
Add: NOTE: placed in *species inquirendae* by Andrássy, 1964 777

PAGE 122

A—*pusillus, Plectus*
Add: NOTE: placed in *species inquirendae* by Meyl, 1961 *1028*

A—*pusillus, Rhodolaimus*
1. Place asterisk before *Rhodolaimus*
2. Add: *valid name according to Goodey, 1963 *881*

A—*pusteri, Plectus*
Add: *1020 = Plectus parietinus* Bastian, 1865

A—*putrefaciens, Tylenchus*
Add: †*Ditylenchus* (Kühn, 1877 or 1879) Filipjev & Schuurmans Stekhoven, 1941 *212*

A—*pygmaea, Dorylaimus*
Add: NOTE: placed in *species inquirendae* by Goodey, 1963 *881*

A—*pygmaea, Tripyla*
Add: NOTE: placed in *species inquirendae* by Brzeski, 1964 *806*

N—*pygmaeum*
Labronema Heyns, 1963 *902*

N—*pygmaeus*
Mylodiscoides Lordello, 1963 *1004*

pygmaeus

A—pygmaeus, Pycnolaimus
Add: Plectus (Cobb, 1920) Maggenti,
1961 1020
NOTE: placed in species inquirendae
by Maggenti, 1961 1020

A—pylophilus, Diplogaster
Add: Mononchoides (Weingärtner,
1955) Goodey, 1963 881

A—pyri, Anguillula
Add: NOTE: (2) placed in species inquirendae by Goodey, 1960 876

PAGE 123

N—quadralata
Ecphyadophora Corbett, 1964 840

N—quadramphidius
Eudorylaimus Andrássy, 1963 774

A,C—quadricorne, Criconema
1. Change species name to quadri-
cornis
2. Add: Macroposthonia (Kirjanova,
1948) de Grisse & Loof, 1965 891

A—quadridentata, Diplogaster
Add: NOTE: placed in species inquirendae by Meyl, 1961 1028

A—quadrilabiatus, Cheilobus
1. Place asterisk before 556
2. Add: *questionable synonymy according to Meyl, 1961 1028

A,C—quarta, Gottholdsteineria
1. Change species name to quartus
2. Add: Rotylenchus (Andrássy, 1958)
Sher, 1961 1065

N—quasidemani
Criconemoides Wu, 1965 1160
Nothocriconema (Wu, 1965) de Grisse
& Loof, 1965 891

A—queirozi, Spirotylenchus
Add: Rotylenchulus (Lordello &
Cesnik, 1958) Loof & Oostenbrink,
1962 1003
881 = Rotylenchulus reniformis Linford & Oliveira, 1940

rarus

C—quercophila, Rhabditis
Delete asterisks and footnote

A—quercophilus, Diplogasteroides
Add: Rhabdontolaimus (Heindl-Mengert, 1956) Meyl, 1961 1028

N—raabei
Plectus Brzeski, 1961 789

A—radicicola, Anguillula
Add: NOTE: (2) probably an Anguina
according to Thorne, 1961 1132

PAGE 124

A—radicicolus, Isonchus
1. Place asterisk before Aphelenchus
2. Add: *valid species according to
Thorne, 1961 1132

N—radulatus
Trachactinolaimus Andrássy, 1963 772

N—rafiqi
Boleodorus Husain & Khan, 1965 919

A—rahmi, Diplogaster
Add: NOTE: placed in species inquirendae by Goodey, 1963 881

N—raoi
Acrobeles Kannan, 1961 958

A—rapax, Mononchus
Add: 753 = Mononchus dadayi Micoletzky, 1914
1032 Mononchus rapax (male only)
of Williams, 1958 = Mononchus
studeri Steiner, 1914

N—rapsoides
Eudorylaimus Heyns & Lagerwey,
1965 908b

N—rapsus
Eudorylaimus Heyns, 1963 904

A—rarus, Diplogaster
Add: Eudiplogaster (Völk, 1950)
Meyl, 1961 1028
Fictor (Völk, 1950) Goodey, 1963
881

A—rarus, Ditylenchus
Add: Neoditylenchus (Meyl, 1954)
Goodey, 1963 881

N—raskiense
Criconemoides de Grisse, 1964 889
Macroposthonia (de Grisse, 1964) de
Grisse & Loof, 1965 891
Neocriconema (de Grisse, 1964) Diab
& Jenkins, 1965 845
Mesocriconema (de Grisse, 1964) An-
drássy, 1965

N—raskii
Criconemoides Goodey, 1963 881
881 syn: Criconemoides mutabile of
Raski, 1952
891 = Criconemoides mutabile Taylor,
1936

N—raskii
Tylencholaimellus Jairajpuri & Siddiqi,
1963 946

A—ratzeburgii, Aphelenchoides
Add: Bursaphelenchus (Rühm, 1956)
Goodey, 1960 876

A—recessus, Mononchus
Add: Sporonchulus (Cobb, 1917)
Mulvey, 1963 1034

N—recurvatus
Acrobeloides Goodey, 1963 881
881 syn: Acrobeloides buetschlii of
Steiner & Buhrer, 1933

N—recurvus
Mesodorylaimus Andrássy, 1964 779

PAGE 125

A—regiusi, var. magna, Thornia
Add: 1028 = Tylencholaimus propinqua Paesler, 1941

N—regulus
Cobbonchus Altherr, 1963 756

N—remyi
Longidorus Altherr, 1963 755
Paralongidorus (Altherr, 1963) Sid-
diqi & Husain, 1965 1106

A—reniformis, Rotylenchulus
Add: 1065 syn: Rotylenchus elisensis
Carvalho, 1957
881 syn: Spirotylenchus queirozi
Lordello & Cesnik, 1958
881 syn: Helicotylenchus parvus
Williams, 1960
881 syn: Leiperotylenchus leiperi
Das, 1960

A—reticulatum, Bunonema
1. Place asterisk before Bunonema
2. Add: *valid genus according to
Goodey, 1963 881

A—retusus, Aphelenchus
Add: NOTE: placed in species inquirendae by Goodey, 1960 876

N—retusus
Helicotylenchus Siddiqi & Brown,
1964 1101

N—reversus
Dorylaimoides Thorne, 1964 1133

A—revoluta, Anthonema
Add: Anonchus (Cobb, 1906) Goodey,
1963 881

A—reynecki, Dorylaimus
Add: †Eudorylaimus (van der Linde,
1938) Andrássy, 1959 50d

N—rhenanus
Mesodorylaimus Altherr, 1965 757a

A—rhenanus, Parasitaphelenchus
Add: NOTE: placed in species inquirendae by Goodey, 1960 876

A—rhizophilus, Diploscapter
Add: 881 syn: Diploscapter rhizophilus, var. cannae Rahm, 1928
881 syn: Diploscapter rhizophilus,
var. cylindricus Rahm, 1928

A,C—rhizophilus, Plectus
1. Delete asterisks and footnote
2. Add: Proteroplectus (de Man,
1880) Paramonov, 1964 1040

A—*rhizophilus,* var. *cannae, Diploscapter*
Add: *881 = Diploscapter rhizophilus*
Rahm, 1928

A—*rhizophilus,* var. *cylindricus, Diploscapter*
Add: *881 = Diploscapter rhizophilus*
Rahm, 1928

N—*rhodesiensis*
Trichodorus Siddiqi & Brown, 1965
1102

A—*rhopalocercus, Metaphelenchus*
Add: *879 = Aphelenchus avenae* Bastian, 1865

N—*rhopalocercus*
Tylenchorhynchus Seinhorst, 1963
1064

A—*richtersi, Aphelenchus*
Add: NOTE: placed in *species inquirendae* by Goodey, 1960 *876*

A—*richtersi, Bunonema*
1. Place asterisk before *Bunonema*
2. Add *valid name according to Goodey, 1963 *881*

N—*riparius*
Dorylaimoides Andrássy, 1962 *771*

N—*ritai*
Tylenchus [*Tylenchus*] Siddiqi, 1963
1083

N—*ritteri*
Hemicycliophora Brizuela, 1963 *785*

A—*rivalis, Aphelenchus*
Add: NOTE: placed in *species inquirendae* by Goodey, 1960 *876*

A—*rivalis, Enoplus*
Add: NOTE: placed in *species inquirendae* by Maggenti, 1961 *1020*

A—*robinicola, Diplogaster*
Add: *Eudiplogaster* (Rühm, 1956)
Meyl, 1961 *1028* (*c*)
Fictor (Rühm, 1956) Goodey, 1963
881

A—*robustum, Dorylaimus*
Add: *994 Dorylaimus robustus* of de
Man, 1884 (male, in part) =
Dorylaimus crassus de Man, 1884
994 = Dorylaimus stagnalis Dujardin, 1845
757a ? *Dorylaimus robustus* of de
Man, 1921 = *Sectonema demani*
Altherr, 1965

A—*robustus, Diplogaster*
Add: NOTE: placed in *species inquirendae* by Goodey, 1963 *881*

A—*robustus, Tylenchus*
Add: *1071 Anguillulina robusta* of
Goodey, 1932 in part, *Rotylenchus robustus* of Filipjev & Schuurmans
Stekhoven, 1941 in part, and Goodey
& Seinhorst, 1960 = *Rotylenchus
fallorobustus* Sher, 1965

N—*rosae*
Criconemoides Loof, 1964 *1000*
Macroposthonia (Loof, 1964) de
Grisse & Loof, 1965 *891*

A—*rostochiensis, Heterodera*
1. Place asterisk before *Heterodera*
2. Add: *valid name according to
Goodey, 1963 *881*

A—*rotundatum, Xiphinema*
1. Place asterisk before *Xiphinema*
2. Add: *Longidorus* (Schuurmans
Stekhoven & Teunissen, 1938)
Goodey, 1963 *881*
*valid genus according to Luc &
Tarjan, 1963 *1019*

N—*rotundicauda*
Criconemoides Loof, 1964 *1000*
Macroposthonia (Loof, 1964) de
Grisse & Loof, 1965 *891*

A—*rotundicauda, Dorylaimus*
Add: *1028 = Carcharolaimus teres*
Thorne, 1939
NOTE: regarded a valid species by
Goodey, 1963 *881*

N—*rotundicaudata*
  Criconemoides Wu, 1965 *1160*
  Macroposthonia (Wu, 1965) de Grisse
  & Loof, 1965 *891*

N—*rotundicaudatus*
  Mononchulus Kannan, 1961 *959*

A—*rotundicephala, Amphispira*
  Add: NOTE: placed in *species inquirendae* by Goodey, 1963 *881*

N—*rotundum*
  Axonchium Thorne, 1964 *1133*

N—*roystoneae*
  Neodiplogaster Lordello & de Oliveira,
  1963 *1005*

PAGE 129

A—*ruehmi, Bunonema*
  Add: *Aspidonema* (Sachs, 1949)
  Goodey, 1963 *881*

N—*ruehmi*
  Bursaphelenchus Baker, 1962 *784*
  784 syn: *Aphelenchoides* [*Bursaphelenchus*] *conjunctus* of Rühm, 1956
  and *Bursaphelenchus conjunctus* of
  Goodey, 1960

C—*ruehmi, Dotylenchus*
  Change genus name to *Dotylaphus*

A—*ruehmi, Panagrodontus*
  Add: *Panagrolaimus* (Ivanova, 1958)
  Goodey, 1963 *881*

N—*ruffoi*
  Panagrolaimus Andrássy, 1962 *768*

N—*rugatocuticulatus*
  Rotylenchus Sher, 1965 *1071*

N—*rugosus*
  Tylenchorhynchus Siddiqi, 1963 *1082*

N—*rumicis*
  Heterodera Poghossian, 1961 *1042*

N—*russi*
  Cheilobus Penso, 1941 *1040b*

A—*rustica, Monhystera*
  Add: NOTE: placed in *species inquirendae* by Meyl, 1961 *1028*

A,C,T—*rusticum, Criconema*
  1. Change species name to *rustica*
  2. Transpose entire entry to immedi-
    ately after *ruricola,* var. *acutus,
    Cyatholaimus*
  3. Add: *Macroposthonia* (Micoletzky,
    1915) de Grisse & Loof, 1965 *891*
    891 syn: *Criconemoides lobatum*
    Raski, 1952
    891 Hoplolaimus rusticus of Stauffer,
    1920 and *Criconemoides rusticum*
    of Taylor, 1936 in part = *Iota
    simile* Cobb, 1918
    1001a Hoplolaimus rusticus of
    Stauffer, 1920 (p. 302) and
    Criconemoides rusticum of Tay-
    lor, 1936 (p. 412) = *Cricone-
    moides xenoplax* Raski, 1952

N—*rusticus*
  Dorylaimoides Timm, 1964 *1140*

A—*ruwenzorii, Actinolaimus*
  Add: *Paractinolaimus* (de Coninck,
  1935) Andrássy, 1964 *781*

A—*ruwenzorii, Dorylaimus*
  1. Place asterisk before *Dorylaimus*
  2. Add: *valid genus according to
    Goodey, 1963 *881*

N—*sacca*
  Belondira Thorne, 1964 *1133*

A—*saccai, Peronilaimus*
  Add: NOTE: placed in *species inquirendae* by Goodey, 1963 *881*

N—*saccatum*
  Axonchium Jairajpuri, 1964 *936*

N—*saccatus*
  Amphorostoma Clark, 1962 *821*
  Proleptonchus (Clark, 1962) Andrássy,
  1963 *772*

N—*sacchari*
  Heterodera Luc & Merny, 1963 *1018*

N—*sacchari*
  Metaphelenchus Akhtar, 1962 *751*
  NOTE: placed in *species inquirendae*
  by Goodey & Hooper, 1965 *879*

N—*sacchari*
  Paralongidorus Siddiqi, Hooper &
  Khan, 1963 *1104*

A—*sachsi, Aphelenchoides*
  Add: *Bursaphelenchus* (Rühm, 1956)
  Goodey, 1960 *876*

N—*sachsi*
  Bunonema [*Aspidonema*] Meyl, 1961
  1028
  1028 syn: *Bunonema* [*Aspidonema*]
  weingaertnerae of Sachs, 1949 in
  part

A—*sachsi, Tylenchus*
  1. Place asterisk before *Tylenchus*
  [*Aglenchus*]
  2. Add: *Aglenchus* (Hirschmann,
  1952) Meyl, 1961 *1028*
  *valid name according to Goodey,
  1963 *881*

N—*sagaensis*
  Criconemoides Yokoo, 1964 *1160c*

PAGE 130

A—*sagittifer, Pharetrolaimus*
  Add: NOTE: placed in *species inquiren-*
  dae by Jairajpuri & Siddiqi, 1963
  946

N—*sali*
  Paralongidorus Siddiqi, Hooper &
  Khan, 1963 *1104*

N—*salina*
  Monhystera Meyl, 1961 *1028*
  1028 syn: *Monhystera filiformis*, var.
  salina Meyl, 1954

A—*salsa, Tripyla*
  Add: NOTE: (2) placed in *species in-*
  quirendae by Brzeski, 1964 *806*

A—*salvus, Miculenchus*
  Add: *Tylenchus* [*Miculenchus*] (Andrássy, 1959) Goodey, 1963 *881*

N—*samarcandicus*
  Chiloplacus Erzhanov, 1964 *852a*

A—*samarcandicus, Dorylaimus*
  Add: *Eudorylaimus* (Tulaganov,
  1949) Andrássy, 1959 *50d*

N—*sandiaensis*
  Ektaphelenchus Massey, 1964 *1025a*

N—*sandneri*
  Tylenchus Wasilewska, 1965 *1145b*

A—*saprophilus, Dorylaimus*
  Add: *Mesodorylaimus* (Peters, 1930)
  Goodey, 1963 *881*

N—*sarissus*
  Paratylenchus Tarjan, 1960 *1124*
  Gracilacus (Tarjan, 1960) Raski, 1962
  1044
  866 = *Procriconema straeleni* de Coninck, 1931

N—*saxeni*
  Paurodontus Husain & Khan, 1965 *915*

N—*sayeedi*
  Tylencholaimellus Siddiqi, 1965 *1098*

A,C—*scandens, Anguillula*
  1. In fifth and sixth lines under species name, change Cobb, 1890 *112*
  to Kühn in Zopf, 1888 *1163*.
  2. Delete note
  3. Place asterisk before *Tylenchus*
  4. Add: *Romanin, 1867 *552* did not
  cite this species. The only mention
  of it in the genus *Tylenchus* I have
  found is in Zopf, 1888 *1163* who
  refers to J. Kühn. Accordingly,
  Kühn in Zopf, 1888 is tentatively
  credited with the combination.

A—*schachtii, Heterodera*
  1. Place asterisk before *Heterodera*
  2. Add: *valid name according to
  Goodey, 1963 *881*
  NOTE: Railliet, 1896 *1043c* sug-
  gested replacement of *Heterodera*
  with *Heterobolbus* because of
  Heteroderes Latreille, 1834.

PAGE 131

A—*scheucherae, Bunonema*
Add: *Aspidonema* (Sachs, 1949) Goodey, 1963 *881*

A,C—*schneideri, Diplogaster*
1. Delete asterisks and footnote
2. Add: *Diplogasteriana* (Paesler, 1939) Meyl, 1961 *1028*

A—*schneideri, Plectus*
Add: NOTE: placed in *species inquirendae* by Meyl, 1961 *1028*

A,C—*schneideri, Rhabditis*
1. In lines 14 and 15 under species name change Andrássy, 1958 *49e* to Goodey, 1953 *294*
2. Delete note
3. Add: *806a* syn: *Altherrnema dibulbosum* Brzeski, 1961

PAGE 132

A—*schwemmlei, Diplogaster*
Add: *Prosodontus* (Sachs, 1950) Goodey, 1963 *881*

N—*scintillans*
Leptonchus Loof, 1964 999
999 syn: *Leptonchus granulosus* of Loof & Oostenbrink, 1962

A—*scleranthii, Heterodera*
Add: NOTE: Goodey, 1963 *881* claims this to be *nomen nudum*. This is justified since Kaktina gave only a nondefinitive length and width value for cysts and presented a figure in which only the general habit of the nematode was shown without morphological detail.

N—*scolyti*
Panagrobelus Massey, 1964 *1025a*

N—*sculptus*
Tylenchorhynchus Seinhorst, 1963 *1064*

A—*secundus, Diplogaster*
Add: *Diplogastrellus* (Bovien, 1937) Meyl, 1961 *1028*

N—*secutum*
Kochinema Siddiqi, 1965 *1098*

A—*selangorensis, Dorylaimus*
Add: *Mesodorylaimus* (de Man, 1929) Goodey, 1963 *881*

C—*serendipiticus, Nacobbus*
Change 1959 to 1960

N—*serendipiticus bolivianus*
Nucobbus Lordello, Zamith & Boock, 1961 *1007*

A—*serenus, Acrobeles*
Add: *Cervidellus* (Kirjanova, 1951) Goodey, 1963 *881*

N—*serenus*
Helicotylenchus Siddiqi, 1963 *1088*

PAGE 133

N—*serpens*
Neotylenchus Andrássy, 1961 767

A—*serpentinus, Dorylaimus*
Add: *Mesodorylaimus* (Thorne & Swanger, 1936) Goodey, 1963 *881*

N—*serrata*
Zeldia Heyns, 1962 900

N—*serratum*
Criconema Khan & Siddiqi, 1963 967
Lobocriconema (Khan & Siddiqi, 1963) de Grisse & Loof, 1965 *891*

N—*setensis*
Eucephalobus Kannan, 1960 955

A,C—*setifera, Tripyla*
1. Delete asterisks and footnote
2. Add: *Trischistoma* (Bütschli, 1873) Altherr, 1965 *757a*

A—*setifera,* var. *triloboides, Tripyla*
Add: NOTE: placed in *varietas inquirendum* by Brzeski, 1964 806

A—*setosa, Cephalobus*
Add: NOTE: regarded a species of doubtful standing by Goodey, 1963 *881*

71

N—setosus
Acrobeloides Brzeski, 1962 795

A,C—setosus, Monhystera
1. Delete lines 13 and 14 under species name, the entry beginning with Theristus
2. Add: *Theristus (Bütschli, 1874) de Man, 1907 432 as entry between lines 3 and 4
*valid genus according to Meyl, 1957 1027a

N—sexamammilatus
Anguillulina Kirjanova, 1938 981
Tylenchorhynchus (Kirjanova, 1938) Kirjanova, 1961 982
NOTE: placed in species inquirendae by Tarjan, 1964 1125

A,C—sexcristatus, Mononchus
1. Change 1950 to 1951
2. Add: Mylonchulus (Merzheevskaya, 1951) Mulvey, 1961 1030

N—sexdentati
Aphelenchoides [Bursaphelenchus] Rühm, 1960 1054
1055a = Bursaphelenchus bakeri Rühm, 1964

A—sexdentati, Panagrolaimus
Add: NOTE: (2) placed in species inquirendae by Meyl, 1961 1028

N—sexdentati
Parasitorhabditis Rühm, 1960 1054

N—sexlineatus
Acrobeloides Brzeski, 1962 795

N—seymouri
Criconema Wu, 1965 1159

PAGE 134

N—sheri
Rotylenchus Jairajpuri, 1964 934
1071 = Rotylenchus buxophilus Golden, 1956

N—sheri
Tripylina Brzeski, 1963 800
Trischistoma (Brzeski, 1963) Brzeski, 1965 807

N—siamense
Scutellonema Timm, 1965 1141

N—sica
Sectonema Clark, 1964 827

N—siddiqii
Criconemoides Khan, 1964 975

N—sigmaturellus
Mylonchulus Mulvey, 1961 1030
1030 syn: Mononchus sigmaturoides Schuurmans Stekhoven, 1943

A—sigmaturoides, Mononchus
Add: 1030 = Mylonchulus sigmaturellus Mulvey, 1961

A—sigmaturus, Mononchus
Add: 1030 syn: Mononchus brachyuris (male) of de Man, 1876 and (female) of de Man, 1884

A,C—silusiae, Anguillula
1. Delete asterisks and footnote
2. Place asterisk before Panagrellus
3. Add: *valid species according to Sanwal, 1960 1058

N—silusioides
Panagrellus Tsalolikhin, 1965 1144b

A—silvatica, Rhabditis
Add: NOTE: placed in species inquirendae by Meyl, 1961 1028 but regarded as a valid species by Goodey, 1963 881

N—silvaticus
Eudorylaimus Brzeski, 1960 787

N—silvaticus
Tylenchorhynchus Ferris, 1963 855

N—silvestris
Dolichodorus Gillespie & Adams, 1962 869

A—silvestris, Dorylaimus
Add: Pungentus (de Man, 1912) Coomans & Geraert, 1962 837
837 syn: Pungentus thornei Goodey, 1943

N—*silvestris*
Hemicycliophora Jenkins & Reed, 1964
952

A,C,T—*simile, Iota*
1. Change species name to *similis*
2. Transpose entire entry to after *similis, Hemicycliophora*
3. Add: *Macroposthonia* (Cobb, 1918) de Grisse & Loof, 1965 *891*
    891 syn: *Criconema beljaevae* Kirjanova, 1948
    891 syn: *Criconema cylindricum* Kirjanova, 1948
    891 syn: *Criconema tenuiannulata* Tulganov, 1949
    891 syn: *Criconemoides xenoplax* Raski, 1952
    891 syn: *Hoplolaimus rusticus* of Stauffer, 1920
    891 syn: *Criconemoides rusticum* of Taylor, 1936 in part

N—*similis*
Boleodorus Khan & Basir, 1963 *963*

A—*similis, Diplogaster*
Add: *Holodiplogaster* (Bütschli, 1876) Meyl, 1961 *1028*
    Fictor (Bütschli, 1876) Goodey, 1963 *881*

A—*similis, Discolaimus*
1. Place asterisk before *Discolaimus*
2. Add: *valid species according to Loof, 1964 *1001*

C—*similis, Dolichodorus*
Change reference number from 225 to 255

PAGE 135

N—*similis*
Dorylaimoides Thorne, 1964 *1133*

N—*similis*
Paurodontus Siddiqi, 1961 *1074*

N—*similis*
Trichodorus Seinhorst, 1963 *1063*

N—*similis*
Tylencholaimus Jairajpuri, 1965 *945*

A—*similis, Tylenchus*
Add: *1091 Radopholus similis* of Williams, 1960 = *Radopholus williamsi* Siddiqi, 1964

N—*simlaensis*
Criconema Jairajpuri, 1963 *927*

A—*simplex, Alaimus*
Add: *766* syn: *Aphanolaimus tenuis* Daday, 1899

A—*simplex, Choronema*
Add: NOTE: (2) placed in *species inquirendae* by Goodey, 1963 *881*

N—*simplex*
Discolaimium Siddiqi, 1965 *1096*

A—*sinensis, Acrobeles*
Add: *761* = *Acrobeles ciliatus* Linstow, 1877

N—*sinensis*
Aphelenchoides Andrássy, 1960 *761*
    761 syn: *Aphelenchus parietinus,* var. *sinensis* Wu & Hoeppli, 1929

A—*sinensis, Hoplolaimus*
Add: NOTE: (2) placed in *species inquirendae* by Andrássy, 1960 *761.*
(3) placed in *incertae sedis* by de Grisse & Loof, 1965 *891*

N—*singhi*
Aphelenchoides Das, 1960 *842*

A—*singularis, Belondira*
Add: NOTE: not a *Belondira* according to Jairajpuri, 1964 *936*

A—*sinodendroni, Aphelenchoides*
Add: *Aphelenchoides* Rühm, 1957 *1060*

PAGE 136

A—*sinodendroni, Diplogaster*
Add: *Koerneria* (Körner, 1954) Meyl, 1961 *1028*

A—*skarbilowiezae, Hexatylus*
Add: *Scytaleum* (Atakhanov, 1958) Andrássy, 1961 *767*
    Neotylenchus (Atakhanov, 1958) Goodey, 1963 *881*

73

N—smithi
  Discolaimoides Heyns, 1963 902
  Discolaimium (Heyns, 1963) Timm &
  Bhuiyan, 1963 1143

N—socialis
  Tylenchorhynchus Andrássy, 1962
  769a

N—solani
  Thornedia Husain & Khan, 1965 916

N—solivaga
  Criconemoides Andrássy, 1962 769a
  Macroposthonia (Andrássy, 1962) de
  Grisse & Loof, 1965 891
  Neocriconema (Andrássy, 1962) Diab
  & Jenkins, 1965 845

N—solus
  Eudorylaimus Andrássy, 1962 770

N—solus
  Mylonchulus Mulvey, 1961 1030

A—southerni, Iota
  Add: Criconema (Schneider, 1940) de
  Coninck, 1943 163
  NOTE: placed in species inquirendae
  by Siddiqi & Goodey, 1964 1103

A—sparsus, Mononchus
  Add: NOTE: placed in species inquirendae by Mulvey, 1961 1030

N—spartinae
  Hypsoperine Rau & Fassuliotis, 1965
  1047

A—speciosus, Aphelenchoides
  1. Place asterisk before Aphelenchoides
  2. Add: Seinura (Andrássy, 1958)
  Goodey, 1960 876
  *regarded as valid genus by Meyl,
  1961 1028 and placed in species
  inquirendae by Hechler & Taylor,
  1965 897

A—spectabilis, Mononchus
  Add: NOTE: Mononchus [Prionchulus]
  spectabilis of Meyl, 1955 is regarded as species inquirenda by
  Clark, 1960 815

A,C—sphaerocephalum, Criconemoides
  1. Change species name to sphaeroce-
  phala
  2. Add: 1001 syn: Criconemoides citri
  Steiner, 1949
  Macroposthonia (Taylor, 1936) de
  Grisse & Loof, 1965 891

A—sphagni, Criconema
  Add: Nothocriconema (Micoletzky,
  1925) de Grisse & Loof, 1965 891

A—sphagni, Diplogaster
  Add: Mononchoides (Soós, 1938)
  Goodey, 1963 881

N—sphagni
  Mononchus Brzeski, 1960 787

N—spicatus
  Dorylaimellus Loof, 1964 1001

N—spicaudatus
  Helicotylenchus Tarjan, 1964 1127

PAGE 137

A,C—spinicaudatus, Tylenchorhynchus
  1. Change species name to spini-
  caudata
  2. Add: Hirschmannia (Schuurmans
  Stekhoven, 1944) Luc & Goodey,
  1962 1014
  1014 syn: Radopholus lavabri Luc,
  1957
  Hirschmanniella (Schuurmans Stekhoven, 1944) Luc & Goodey,
  1964 1015

N—spinocaudatus
  Aphelenchoides Skarbilovich, 1957
  1112
  NOTE: regarded a valid species by
  Brzeski, 1962 791

N—spiralis
  Mydonomus Thorne, 1964 1133

A—spiralis, Tylenchus
  Add: 1065 = Tylenchus dihystera
  Cobb, 1893

A—splendidus, Diplogaster
  Add: Mononchoides (Körner, 1954)
  Goodey, 1963 881

A,C—squamosum, Iota
1. Change species name to *squamosus*
2. Delete asterisks and footnote
3. Add: *Hemicriconemoides* (Cobb, 1913) Siddiqi & Goodey, 1964 *1103*
   1103 syn: *Hemicriconemoides mangiferae* Siddiqi, 1961
   1103 syn: *Hemicriconemoides strictathecatus* Esser, 1960

A—stagnalis, Dorylaimus
Add: *994* syn: *Dorylaimus robustus* de Man, 1876

A—stagnalis, Monhystera
Add: *761* syn: *Monhystera wangi* Wu & Hoeppli, 1929

PAGE 138

A,C—stagnalis fecundus, var. pseudo-crassus, Dorylaimus
1. Delete asterisks and footnote
2. Add: *995* = *Dorylaimus crassus* de Man, 1884

N—stakmani
Rotylenchulus Husain & Khan, 1965 *917*

A—stammeri, Aphelenchoides
1. Place asterisk before *Aphelenchoides*
2. Add: *Ektaphelenchus* (Körner, 1954) Goodey, 1960 *876*
   *valid genus according to Meyl, 1961 *1028*

PAGE 139

A—stammeri, Diplogaster
Add: *Diplogastrellus* (Weingärtner, 1955) Meyl, 1961 *1028*

A—stammeri, Sphaerulariopsis
1. Place asterisk before *Sphaerulariopsis*
2. Add: *valid genus according to Nickle, 1963 *1036*

A,C—stancowici, Diplogaster
1. Change species name to *stankowici*
2. Change Schneider, 1932 *575* to Schneider in Stanković, 1932 *1116a*
3. Add: NOTE: believed to be a *nomen nudum* by Goodey, 1963 *881*

N—stefanskii
Witoldinema Brzeski, 1960 *787*
Labronema (Brzeski, 1960) Goodey, 1963 *881*

A—steineri, Aphelenchoides
1. Place asterisk before *Aphelenchoides*
2. Add: *Bursaphelenchus* (Rühm, 1956) Goodey, 1960 *876*
   *valid genus according to Meyl, 1961 *1028*

A—steineri, Bunonema
1. Place asterisk before *Bunonema* in line 1
2. Add: *valid name according to Goodey, 1963 *881*

A—steineri, Cephalobus
Add: *Eucephalobus* (Andrássy, 1952) Goodey, 1963 *881*

N—steineri
Hoplolaimus Kannan, 1961 *958*

N—steineri
Paratylenchus Golden, 1961 *870*
Gracilacus (Golden, 1961) Raski, 1962 *1044*
*valid genus according to Siddiqi & Goodey, 1964 *1103*

A—steineri, Pratylenchus
Add: *993* = *Tylenchus brachyurus* Godfrey, 1929

N—steineri
Seinura Hechler in Hechler & Taylor, 1965 *897*
897 syn: *Aphelenchus tenuicaudatus* of Steiner, 1927 and Goodey, 1928

A—steineri, Tylencholaimus
Add: *Thorneela* (Schneider, 1925) Goodey, 1963 *881*

A—stenodorus, Dorylaimoides
Add: NOTE: Siddiqi, 1964 *1093* credited Hopper & Cairns, 1959 *322c* as having transferred this species to *Dorylaimus*. Inspection of the latter work shows this action to be a *lapsus calami* and not an intention n. comb.

N—*stephanus*
Hoplolaimus Sher, 1963 *1066*

PAGE 140

A—*stercorarius, Diplogaster*
Add: *Holodiplogaster* (Bovien, 1937)
Meyl, 1961 *1028*
Fictor (Bovien, 1937) Goodey,
1963 *881*

A,C—*steueri, Aphelenchus*
1. Change note to: suppression of this
name requested by Sher, 1965 *1070*
2. Add: *Helicotylenchus* (Stefański,
1916) Sher, 1961 *1065*

N—*stictochroum*
Isolaimium Timm, 1961 *1137a*

A—*stigmatus, Diplogasteroides*
1. Place asterisk before *Diplogasteroides*
2. Add: *Rhabdontolaimus* (Steiner,
1930) Meyl, 1961 *1028*
*valid genus according to Massey,
1962 *1024*

A—*stoeckherti, Diplogaster*
1. Place asterisk before *Diplogasteritus*
2. Add: *valid genus according to
Meyl, 1961 *1028*

A—*straeleni, Procriconema*
Add: *Paratylenchus* (de Coninck,
1931) Oostenbrink, 1960 *1038*
866 syn: *Paratylenchus sarissus*
Tarjan, 1960
NOTE: placed in *species inquirendae*
by Siddiqi & Goodey, 1964 *1103*

A—*strandicornutus, Cephalobus*
Add: *Cephalobus* [*Heterocephalobus*]
Allgén, 1934 *786*
Heterocephalobus (Allgén, 1934)
Brzeski, 1961 *788*

A—*strenzkei, Hemicycliophora*
Add: *Paratylenchus* (Volz, 1951)
Oostenbrink, 1960 *1038*
NOTE: (1) regarded *incertae sedis*
by Tarjan, 1960 *1124*
(2) placed in *species inquirendae*
by Meyl, 1961 *1028* (*c*)

(3) regarded a possible synonym of
Procriconema straeleni by Geraert,
1965 *866*

N—*striata*
Poncenema Thorne, 1964 *1133*

A—*striata, Tylopharynx*
Add: *881* = *Aphelenchus foetidus*
Bütschli, 1874

A—*striatulus, Diplogaster*
Add: *Eudiplogaster* (Fuchs, 1933)
Meyl, 1961 *1028*
Mononchoides (Fuchs, 1933)
Goodey, 1963 *881*

PAGE 141

A,C,T—*striatum, Paraxonchium*
1. Change species name to *striatus*
2. Transpose entire entry to immediately after *striatus, Mononchus*
3. Add: *Drepanodorus* (Krall, 1958)
Clark, 1961 *815b*

A—*striatus, Actinolaimus*
Add: *Actinca* (Thorne, 1939) Andrássy, 1964 *781*

N—*striatus*
Alaimus Loof, 1964 *1001*

A—*striatus, Anguillonema*
Add: *Neoditylenchus* (Fuchs, 1938)
Meyl, 1961 *1028*

A—*striatus, Aphelenchus*
Add: NOTE: placed in *species inquirendae* by Goodey, 1960 *876*

A—*striatus, Diplogaster*
Add: *Mononchoides* (Bütschli, 1876)
Goodey, 1963 *881*

A—*striatus, Iotalaimus*
Add: NOTE: placed in *species inquirendae* by Goodey, 1963 *881*

N—*striatus*
Tylenchus Das, 1960 *842*
Tylenchus [*Filenchus*] Das, 1960 *881*

N—*striatus*
Tyleptus Heyns, 1963 *903*

N—*strictathecatus*
   Hemicriconemoides Esser, 1960 *853*
   Hemicycliophora (Esser, 1960)
     Goodey, 1963 *881*
   1103 = *Iota squamosus* Cobb, 1913

PAGE 142

A—*studeri, Mononchus*
   Add: *1032* syn: *Mononchus rapax*
   (male) of Williams, 1958

A,C—*stygia, Criconema*
   1. Change species name to *stygium*
   2. Add: *Nothocriconema* (Schneider,
     1940) de Grisse & Loof, 1965 *891*
     781b syn: *Criconemoides hygro-*
     philum Goodey, 1963

A—*styriacum, Craspedonema*
   1. Place asterisk before *Craspedonema*
   2. Add: *valid name according to
     Goodey, 1963 *881*

N—*subacutus*
   Anatonchus Mulvey, 1961 *1031*

A—*subacutus, Dorylaimus*
   Add: †*Eudorylaimus* (Altherr, 1952)
   Andrássy, 1959 *50d*

A—*subamericanus, Diplogaster*
   Add: *Prosodontus* (van der Linde,
   1938) Goodey, 1963 *881*

A—*subaquilus, Brasilaimus*
   Add: *Actinolaimus* (Lordello &
   Zamith, 1957) Clark, 1961 *815b*

N—*subclavatus*
   Nygellus Timm & Ameen, 1960 *1142*

A—*subdentatus, Diplogaster*
   Add: *Koerneria* (Gunhold, 1952)
   Meyl, 1961 *1028*
   *questionably placed in genus by
   Meyl, 1961 *1028*

N—*subdigiticaudatus*
   Aporcelaimus Altherr, 1965 *757a*

A—*sublabiatus, Dorylaimus*
   Add: *Aporcelaimus* (Thorne &
   Swanger, 1936) Brzeski, 1962 *794*

N—*sublatum*
   Discolaimium Heyns, 1963 *902*

A—*submersus, Plectus*
   1. Place asterisk before *Plectus*
   2. Add: *Anaplectus* (Hirschmann,
     1952) Maggenti, 1961 *1020*
     *valid genus according to Goodey,
     1963 *881*

A—*submissus, Dorylaimus*
   Add: †*Eudorylaimus* (Kirjanova,
   1951) Andrássy, 1959 *50d*

N—*subparietinus*
   Aphelenchoides Sanwal, 1961 *1061*

PAGE 143

N—*subtenuis*, var. *bionchus*
   Mononchus [*Mylonchulus*] Kannan,
   1961 *957*

N—*subtenuis*, var. *subventralis*
   Mononchus [*Mylonchulus*] Kannan,
   1961 *956*

A—*subterraneus, Diplogaster*
   Add: *Anchidiplogaster* (Hnatewytsch,
   1929) Meyl, 1961 *1028*
   Diplogasteritus (Hnatewytsch, 1929)
   Goodey, 1963 *881*

A—*subulatus, Dorylaimus*
   Add: *Aporcelaimus* (Cobb in Thorne
   & Swanger, 1936) Brzeski, 1962 *794*

N—*sulcatum*
   Criconema Golden & Friedman, 1964
   873
   Lobocriconema (Golden & Friedman,
   1964) de Grisse & Loof, 1965 *891*

A—*sumatrensis, Brachonchulus*
   Add: NOTE: placed in *species inquiren-*
   dae by Mulvey, 1963 *1034*

PAGE 144

N—*sundarus*
   Eudorylaimus Williams, 1964 *1149*

A—*superbus, Diplogaster*
   1. Place asterisk before *Diplogasteritus*
   2. Add: *valid genus according to
     Meyl, 1961 *1028*

77

superbus

A—superbus, Dorylaimus
Add: 1028 syn: Aporcelaimus parvus
Altherr in Lordello, 1955

A—sychnus, Aphelenchoides
Add: Bursaphelenchus (Rühm, 1956)
Goodey, 1960 876

A—sycobius, Tylenchus
Add: NOTE: placed in species inquirendae by Meyl, 1961 1028

A—sylphus, Dorylaimus
Add: Mesodorylaimus (Thorne, 1939)
Goodey, 1963 881

N—sylvaticus
Amphidelus Siddiqi & Basir, 1965 1100

A—systenoceri, Diplogaster
Add: Koerneria (Körner, 1954) Meyl,
1961 1028

N—szechenyii
Mesodorylaimus Andrássy, 1961 766a

N—szekessyi
Mesodorylaimus Andrássy, 1960 761

N—szunyoghyi
Mesorhabditis Andrássy, 1961 766a

A—tabacum, Heterodera
1. Place asterisk before Heterodera
2. Add: 984 Heterodera tabacum of
Kirjanova, 1959 = Heterodera
pseudorostochiensis Kirjanova, 1963
*valid name according to Goodey,
1963 881

N—tadshikistanica
Meloidogyne Kirjanova & Ivanova,
1965 984a

N—taeda
Acrostichus Massey, 1962 1024
Filipjevella (Massey, 1962) Laza-
revskaja, 1965 990c

N—tafazzuli
Diphtherophora Husain, Khan &
s'Jacob, 1965 921

tener

N—taleolus
Anguillulina Kirjanova, 1938 981
Ditylenchus (Kirjanova, 1938) Kir-
janova, 1961 982

A—talonus, Aphelenchoides
Add: Bursaphelenchus (Thorne, 1935)
Massey, 1956 1023

N—taniwha
Longidorus Clark, 1963 823

N—taomasinae
Mesotylus de Guiran, 1964 894
Pratylenchoides (de Guiran, 1964)
Tarjan & Weischer, 1965 1129

N—tarjani
Ecphyadophora Husain & Khan, 1965
915

N—tarjani
Hemicyliophora Khan & Basir, 1963
964

N—tarjani
Longidorus Siddiqi, 1962 1079

PAGE 145

A—tatrica, Tripyla
Add: 799 = Tripyla affinis de Man,
1880

N—tausaghyzatus
Anguillulina Kirjanova, 1938 981
Ditylenchus (Kirjanova, 1938) Kirja-
nova, 1961 982

N—taylori
Criconema Jairajpuri, 1964 929

N—taylori
Macroposthonia de Grisse & Loof,
1965 891
891 syn: Criconemoides annulatum
Taylor, 1936

A—tenax, Monhystera
Add: NOTE: placed in species inquirendae by Meyl, 1961 1028

N—tener
Tylenchorhynchus Erzhanov, 1964
852a

78

A—*tentaculatum, Plectus*
Add: NOTE: placed in *species inquirendae* by Meyl, 1961 *1028*, but also listed as a valid species by the same author

N—*tenue*
Discolaimium Furstenberg & Heyns, 1965 *863a*

A—*tenuiaculeatus, Dorylaimus*
Add: *Actinca* (Kreis, 1924) Andrássy, 1964 *781*

A—*tenuiannulata, Criconema*
Add: *891* = *Iota simile* Cobb, 1918

A—*tenuicauda, Tripyla*
Add: NOTE: placed in *species inquirendae* by Brzeski, 1964 *806*

N—*tenuicaudatum*
Criconema Siddiqi, 1961 *1077*

A,C,T—*tenuicaudatus, Aphelenchus*
1. Change species name to *tenuicaudata*
2. Delete asterisks and footnote
3. Transpose entire entry to immediately after *tenuicauda, Tripyla*
4. Add: *876 Aphelenchoides tenuicaudatus* of Christie, 1939 = *Seinura christiei* Goodey, 1960
Seinura (de Man, 1895) Goodey, 1960 *876*
896 syn: *Seinura christiei* Goodey, 1960
897 Aphelenchus tenuicaudatus of Steiner, 1927 and Goodey, 1928 = *Seinura steineri* Hechler in Hechler & Taylor, 1965

A,C—*tenuicaudatus, Dorylaimus*
1. Delete asterisks and footnote
2. Add: *Mesodorylaimus* (Bastian, 1865) Goodey, 1963 *881*

N—*tenuicaudatus*
Oxydirus Thorne, 1964 *1133*

N—*tenuicaudatus*
Paratylenchus Wu, 1961 *1154*

A—*tenuicaudatus, Udonchus*
Add: NOTE: placed in *species inquirendae* by Goodey, 1963 *881*

A,C—*tenuicute, Criconema*
1. Change species name to *tenuicutis*
2. Add: *Macroposthonia* (Kirjanova, 1948) de Grisse & Loof, 1965 *891*

N—*tenuidens*
Belondira Thorne, 1964 *1133*

A—*tenuidentatus, Mononchus*
Add: *Iotonchus* (Kreis, 1924) Clark, 1961 *816*
NOTE: The name *I. tenuicaudatus* (Kreis, 1924) on p. 261 of Clark, 1961 *816* is a *lapsus calami.*

A—*tenuipunctatus, Diplogaster*
Add: NOTE: placed in *species inquirendae* by Meyl, 1961 *1028*

A—*tenuis, Adorus*
Add: NOTE: placed in *species inquirendae* by Goodey, 1963 *881*

A—*tenuis, Aphanolaimus*
Add: *766* = *Alaimus simplex* Cobb, 1914

N—*tenuis*
Chronogaster Loof & Jairajpuri, 1965 *1002*

A—*tenuis, Diplogaster*
Add: *Anchidiplogaster* (?) (Schneider, 1923) Meyl, 1961 *1028*
NOTE: placed in *species inquirendae* by Goodey, 1963 *881*

N—*tenuis*
Ecphyadophoroides Corbett, 1964 *840*

A—*tenuis, Plectus*
Add: *Proteroplectus* (Bastian, 1865) Paramonov, 1964 *1040*
798 Plectus tenuis of Chodorowska, 1959 and 1961, and of Kozlowska, 1962 in part = *Plectus palustris* Bastian, 1865
798 Plectus tenuis of Kozlowska, 1962 in part = *Plectus cirratus* Bastian, 1865 (*c*)

NOTE: placed in *species inquirendae* by Maggenti, 1961 *1020*

N—tenuis
Tripyla Brzeski, 1964 *806*

N—tenuis
Tylenchus [*Tylenchus*] Kischke, 1956 *881*
881 syn: *Tylenchus* [*Tylenchus*] *davainei tenuis* Kischke, 1956
NOTE (by author): Preempted by *Tylenchus tenuis* Micoletzky, 1922

A—teres, Aphelenchus
Add: NOTE: placed in *species inquirendae* by Sanwal, 1961 *1060*

N—teres
Belondirella Thorne, 1964 *1133*

A—teres, Carcharolaimus
Add: **1028* syn: *Dorylaimus rotundicaudatus* de Man, 1880
**invalid synonymy according to Goodey, 1963 *881*

A—teres, Criconemoides
Add: *Macroposthonia* (Raski, 1952) de Grisse & Loof, 1965 *891*

PAGE 148

N—teres
Proleptonchus Jairajpuri, 1964 *937*

N—teres
Trichodorus Hooper, 1962 *910*
912 syn: *Trichodorus flevensis* Kuiper & Loof, 1962

N—tescorum
Criconemoides de Guiran, 1963 *892*
Macroposthonia (de Guiran, 1963) de Grisse & Loof, 1965 *891*

PAGE 149

A—thalenhorsti, Fuchsia
Add: *Mikoletzkya* (Rühm, 1956) Baker, 1962 *784*

C—thalenhorsti palliati, Diplogaster
Delete entire entry

C—thalenhorsti thalenhorsti, Diplogaster
Delete entire entry

N—thamesi
Meloidogyne Chitwood in Chitwood, Specht & Havis, 1952 *881*
881 syn: *Meloidogyne arenaria thamesi* Chitwood in Chitwood, Specht, & Havis, 1952

N—thecolaimus
Dorylaimoides Heyns, 1963 *903*

A—thermae, Dorylaimus
Add: *Mesodorylaimus* (Cobb in Hoeppli, 1926) Goodey, 1963 *881*

A—thermophilus, Cephalobus
1. Place asterisk before *Cephalobus*
2. Add: *Cephalobus* [*Cephalobus*] Meyl, 1953 *786*
**valid name according to Meyl, 1961 *1028*

A—thienemanni, Dorylaimus
Add: NOTE: regarded as *species inquirenda* by Siddiqi, 1965 *1098a*

A—thienemanni, Hoplolaimus
Add: NOTE: placed in *species inquirendae* by Siddiqi & Goodey, 1964 *1103*

N—thornei
Acrobeles Heyns, 1962 *900*

N—thornei
Acrobeloides Brzeski, 1962 *795*

A—thornei, Funaria
Add: *Leptonchus* (van der Linde, 1938) Andrássy, 1963 *772*

N—thornei
Helicotylenchus Román, 1965 *1052*

N—thornei
Hemicycliophora Goodey, 1963 *881*
881 syn: *Hemicycliophora typica* of Thorne, 1955

N—thornei
Leptonema Jairajpuri, 1964 *933*

A–*thornei, Neotylenchus*
Add: *Scytaleum* (Meyl, 1954) Andrássy, 1961 *767*

N–*thornei*
Nordia Jairajpuri & Siddiqi, 1964 *950*
1090a = *Longidorella xenura* Khan &
Siddiqi, 1963

A,C–*thornei, Pungentus*
1. Change 1942 to 1943
2. Add: *837* = Dorylaimus silvestris de
Man, 1912

N–*thornei*
Tylencholaimellus Husain & Khan,
1965 *920*

A–*thornei, Tylenchus*
Add: *Aglenchus* (Andrássy, 1954)
Meyl, 1961 *1028*
Tylenchus [*Filenchus*] (Andrássy,
1954) Andrássy, 1963 *772*

A–*tigrodon, Panagrolaimus*
1. Place asterisk before *Panagrolaimus*
2. Add: *valid genus according to
Meyl, 1961 *1028*

N–*tlaxcalcensis*
Acrobeloides Flores-Barroeta & Hil-
dago-Escalante, 1961 *859*

A–*tobaensis, Ditylenchus*
Add: *881* = *Anguillula dipsaci* Kühn,
1857

N–*togoensis*
Metacrobeles Loof, 1962 *997*

PAGE 150

A–*toledoi, Acrostichus*
Add: NOTE: placed in *species inquirendae* by Goodey, 1963 *881*

N–*topali*
Chiloplacus Andrássy, 1963 *774*

N–*topayi*
Panagrobelus Andrássy, 1960 *764*

A–*torpidus, Dorylaimus*
Add: NOTE: (2) placed in *species inquirendae* by Meyl, 1961 *1028*

N–*transkeiensis*
Iotonchus Heyns & Lagerwey, 1965
908c

N–*transvaalensis*
Hemicycliophora Heyns, 1962 *901*

N–*transvaalensis*
Leptonchus Heyns, 1963 *903*

N–*tremebunda*
Anguilluloides Goodey, 1963 *881*
881 syn: *Anguilluloides procera* of
Rühm, 1956

A–*trichiuroides, Diplogaster*
Add: *Mononchoides* (Schneider, 1937)
Goodey, 1963 *881*

N–*trichodorus*
Nygolaimus Andrássy, 1965 *781a*

A–*trichuris, Diplogaster*
Add: *Mononchoides* (Cobb, 1893)
Goodey, 1963 *881*

N–*trichurus*
Amphidelus Siddiqi & Brown, 1965
1102

A–*trichurus, Mononchus*
Add: *826 Mononchus* [*Iotonchus*] *trichurus* of Allgén, 1929 and *Iotonchus trichurus* of Mulvey, 1963 in
part = *Iotonchus percivali* Clark,
1961

A–*tricincta, Rhabditis*
Add: *881* = *Pelodera axei* Cobbold,
1884

A–*tridentatus, Diplogaster*
Add: NOTE: placed in *species inquirendae* by Goodey, 1963 *881*

A,C–*tridentatus, Mononchus*
1. On lines 6 and 7 under species
name change Altherr, 1953 *34* to
de Coninck, 1939 *161a*
2. Add: *1028 Mononchus* [*Anatonchus*] *tridentatus* of Kreis, 1924 =
Anatonchus kreisi Meyl, 1961

N–*trifolii*
Ditylenchus Skarbilovich, 1957 *1112*

trifurcatus

A,C—*trifurcatus, Acrobeles*
1. Change species name to *trifurcata*
2. Add: *Zeldia* (Thorne, 1925) Goodey, 1963 *881*

N—*triglyphus*
Tylenchorhynchus Seinhorst, 1963 *1064*

N—*trilineatus*
Tylenchorhynchus Timm, 1963 *1139*

PAGE 151

A—*triplogaster, Plectus*
Add: NOTE: (2) regarded as *nomen dubium* by Maggenti, 1961 *1020*.
(3) placed in *species inquirendae* by Meyl, 1961 *1028*

A—*tripum, Ogma*
Add: *1103* syn: *Criconema lentiforme* of de Coninck, 1945

A—*tritici, Dorylaimus*
Add: NOTE: *Dorylaimus tritici* of de Man, 1876 placed in *species inquirendae* by Loof, 1961 *995*

A—*tritici, Plectus*
Add: NOTE: (2) placed in *species inquirendae* by Meyl, 1961 *1028*

N—*trivialis*
Aphelenchoides Franklin & Siddiqi, 1963 *863*

N—*tropicus*
Helicotylenchus Román, 1965 *1052*

N—*tropicus*
Oxydirus Thorne, 1964 *1133*

N—*truncatum*
Scutellonema Sher, 1964 *1067*

PAGE 152

N—*truncatus*
Helicotylenchus Román, 1965 *1052*

A—*tuerkorum, Bunonema*
Add: *Bunonema* Sachs, 1949 *881*

ulmi

N—*tulaganovae*
Eudorylaimus Erzhanov, 1964 *852a*

A—*tulaganovi, Criconema*
Add: *Macroposthonia* (Kirjanova, 1948) de Grisse & Loof, 1965 *891*

N—*tumidus*
°Psilenchus Colbran, 1960 *830*
°doubtful position according to Siddiqi, 1963 *1085*

N—*tunisiensis*
Helicotylenchus Siddiqi, 1964 *1090*

N—*tunisiensis*
Trichodorus Siddiqi, 1963 *1087*

N—*turcicum*
Xiphinema Luc & Dalmasso, 1964 *1013*

PAGE 153

A—*typica, Hemicycliophora*
Add: *881 Hemicycliophora typica* of Thorne, 1955 = *Hemicycliophora thornei* Goodey, 1963

A—*typica, Rhabditis*
Add: NOTE: placed in *species inquirendae* by Meyl, 1961 *1028*

C,T—*typicus, Walcherenia*
1. Change species name to *typica*
2. Transpose entire entry to just after *typica, Rhabditis*

N—*uberrinus*
Acrobeloides Anderson, 1965 *758*

N—*ubis*
Mylonchulus Clark, 1961 *820*

A—*uliginosa, Rhabditis*
Add: NOTE: placed in *species inquirendae* by Meyl, 1961 *1028*

A—*ulmi, Cylindrogaster*
1. Place asterisk before *Goodeyus*
2. Add: °valid name according to Meyl, 1961 *1028*

N—*ulmi*
Laimaphelenchus Khan, 1960 *972*

82

uncinatus

A—*uncinatus, Tylenchus*
1. Place asterisk before *Parasitaphelenchus*
2. Add *876* syn: *Parasitaphelenchus ateri* Fuchs, 1937
   876 syn: *Parasitaphelenchus [Parasitaphelenchus] uncinatus ateri* Fuchs, 1937
   *valid genus according to Goodey, 1960 *876*

PAGE 154

A—*uncinatus ateri, Parasitaphelenchus*
Add: *876* = *Tylenchus uncinatus* (Fuchs, 1929) Fuchs, 1929

N—*undulatus*
Acrobeles Loof, 1964 *1001*

N—*ungulacaudus*
Sphaerularia Khan, 1957 *971*
Stictylus (Khan, 1957) Khan, 1960 *973*
Sphaerulariopsis (Khan, 1957) Nickle, 1963 *1036*

A,C—*uniformis, Hoplolaimus*
1. Delete asterisks and footnote
2. Add: *880* syn: *Tylenchus robustus* of de Man, 1880, 1884 (?), 1917
   *†*Rotylenchus* (Thorne, 1949) Loof & Oostenbrink, 1958 *391b*
   *valid genus according to Sher, 1961 *1065*

A—*unipapillatus, Dorylaimus*
Add: *Mesodorylaimus* (Daday, 1905) Goodey, 1963 *881*

N—*unisexus*
Rotylenchus Sher, 1965 *1071*

N—*unum*
Scutellonema Sher, 1964 *1067*

N—*ureshinoensis*
Hemicriconemoides Yokoo, 1963 *1160a*

N—*utriculoides*
Longidorus Corbett, 1964 *841*
Paralongidorus (Corbett, 1964) Siddiqi & Husain, 1965 *1106*

varicaudatus

N—*vaccinium*
Hemicycliophora Reed & Jenkins, 1963 *1048*
1164 syn: *Hemicycliophora gracilis* of Zuckerman, 1961

N—*vadensis*
Criconemoides Loof, 1964 *1000*
Macroposthonia (Loof, 1964) de Grisse & Loof, 1965 *891*

N—*vaginatum*
Axonchium Jairajpuri, 1965 *938a*

N—*validum*
Scutellonema Sher, 1964 *1067*

A,T—*valkanovi, Tylenchus*
1. Transpose entire entry to just after *uzbekistanicus, Dorylaimus*
2. Place asterisk before *Tylenchus*
3. Add: *Filenchus* (Andrássy, 1958) Meyl, 1961 *1028*
   *valid name according to Goodey, 1963 *881*

N—*vandenbrandei*
Paratylenchus de Grisse, 1962 *884*

N—*vanderlindei*
Xiphinema Heyns, 1962 *898*

A,C—*variabilis, Acrobeles*
1. Place asterisk before *Pseudacrobeles*
2. Delete note
3. Add: *valid genus according to Geraert, 1962 *864*

A—*variabilis, Diplogasteroides*
1. Place asterisk before *Diplogasteroides*
2. Add: *valid genus according to Massey, 1962 *1024*

N—*varians*
Plectus Maggenti, 1961 *1020*
Proteroplectus (Maggenti, 1961) Paramonov, 1964 *1040*

N—*variatus*
Yunqueus Thorne, 1964 *1133*

N—*varicaudatus*
Helicotylenchus Yuen, 1964 *1162*

N—*variocaudatus*
   Rotylenchoides Luc, 1960 *1009*

PAGE 155

A—*velata, Rhabditis*
   Add: *922 = Rhabditis marina* Bastian, 1865

A,C—*velox, Plectus*
   1. Add: *1020 = Plectus parietinus* Bastian, 1865
   2. Change note to: placed in *species inquirendae* by Meyl, 1961 *1028*

N—*venezolanus*
   Mononchus Loof, 1964 *1001*

A—*ventralis, Mononchulus*
   Add *577 = Prismatolaimus nodicaudatus* Daday, 1899

N—*ventralis*
   Telotylenchus Loof, 1963 *998*

A—*ventrodentata, Anguillula*
   Add: *Panagrellus* (Heindl-Mengert, 1956) Baker, 1962 *784*

N—*verrucosus*
   Eucephalobus Kannan, 1960 *955*

N—*verrucosus*
   Pareudesmoscolex Weischer, 1962 *1146*

N—*veruculatus*
   Paratylenchus Wu, 1962 *1156*

N—*vestibularis*
   Peplorhabditis Ivanova, 1960 *924*

A—*vestibulifer, Enchodelus*
   Add: NOTE: placed in *species inquirendae* by Meyl, 1961 *1028*

N—*vexator*
   Dorylaimellus Heyns, 1964 *906*

PAGE 156

N—*viduus*
   Tylencholaimus Jairajpuri, 1965 *945*

A—*vigissi, Hexatylus*
   Add: *Scytaleum* (Skarbilovich, 1952) Andrássy, 1961 *767*
   Neotylenchus (Skarbilovich, 1952) Goodey, 1963 *881*

A—*villosus, Aphelenchus*
   Add: NOTE: placed in *species inquirendae* by Goodey, 1960 *876*

A—*vindobonensis, Plectus*
   Add: *Proteroplectus* (Gunhold, 1953) Paramonov, 1964 *1040*

N—*vineacola*
   Longidorus Sturhan & Weischer, 1964 *1121*

N—*vinealis*
   Desmoscolex Weischer, 1962 *1146*

N—*viriosum*
   Thornenema Williams, 1964 *1150*

N—*virtudesae*
   Ditylenchus Tobar Jiménez, 1964 *1144a*

N—*viruliferus*
   Trichodorus Hooper, 1963 *911*

A—*viviparus, Hexatylus*
   Add: *1028* syn: *Hexatylus brevicaudatus* Meyl, 1954
   1028 syn: *Hexatylus dipapillatus* Meyl, 1954

PAGE 157

N—*vixamictus*
   Dorylaimus Andrássy, 1962 *770*

N—*volutus*
   Boleodorus Lima & Siddiqi, 1963 *992*

A—*vorax, Aporcelaimus*
   Add: *Drepanodorus* (Thorne & Swanger, 1936) Brzeski, 1964 *805*

A—*vorax, Diplogaster*
   1. Place asterisk before *Fictor*
   2. Add: *Holodiplogaster* (Goodey, 1929) Meyl, 1961 *1028* (*c*)

vorax

881 syn: *Diplogaster longisetosus* Paesler, 1946
*valid genus according to Goodey, 1963 *881*

A—*vorax, Mononchus* [*Mononchus*]
Add: *Iotonchus* (Cobb, 1917) Mulvey, 1963 *1033*

N—*voulliemei*
Bunonema [*Rhodolaimus*] Rühm, 1962 *1055*

N—*vuittenezi*
Xiphinema Luc, Lima, Weischer, & Flegg, 1964 *1017*

N—*vulgare*
Xiphinema Tarjan, 1964 *1126*

N—*vulgaris*
Helicotylenchus Yuen, 1964 *1162*

N—*vulgaris*
Tylenchus Brzeski, 1963 *801*
801 syn: *Tylenchus filiformis* of Andrássy, 1954

N—*vulvapillatus*
Iotonchus Andrássy, 1964 *781*

A—*wangi, Monhystera*
Add: *761 = Monhystera stagnalis* Bastian, 1865

N—*warriari*
Lordellonema Jairajpuri, 1965 *943*

A—*weidenbachi, Tylenchus*
1. Place asterisk before *Tylenchus*
2. Add: *regarded as valid name by Goodey, 1963 *881*

A—*weingaertnerae, Bunonema*
Add: *1028 Bunonema* [*Aspidonema*] *weingaertnerae* of Sachs, 1949 in part = *Bunonema* [*Aspidonema*] *sachsi* Meyl, 1961

A—*weingaertnerae, Fuchsia*
Add: *Mikoletzkya* (Rühm, 1956) Baker, 1962 *784*

winchesi

PAGE 158

A—*weissi, Heterodera*
1. Place asterisk before *Heterodera*
2. Add: *valid name according to Goodey, 1963 *881*

N—*wesleyi*
Rhabditolaimus Massey, 1962 *1024*

A—*wessoni, Hemicriconemoides*
1. Place asterisk before *Hemicriconemoides*
2. Add: *Hemicycliophora* (Chitwood & Birchfield, 1957) Goodey, 1963 *881*
*valid genus according to Siddiqi & Goodey, 1964 *1103*

N—*whitei*
Telotylenchus Fisher, 1965 *858*

N—*whittoni*
Sphaeronema Sledge & Christie, 1962 *1115*

N—*wilfordi*
Bursaphelenchus Massey, 1964 *1025a*

N—*wilhelmschneideri*
Aporcelaimus Altherr, 1965 *757a*

N—*williamsi*
Radopholus Siddiqi, 1964 *1091*
1091 syn: *Radopholus similis* of Williams, 1960

A,C—*winchesi, Aphelenchus*
1. Delete asterisks and footnote
2. Add: *Seinura* (Goodey, 1927) Goodey, 1960 *876*

A—*winchesi, Diplogaster*
Add: *Holodiplogaster* (Goodey, 1929) Meyl, 1961 *1028*
Fictor (Goodey, 1929) Goodey, 1963 *881*

A—*winchesi*, var. *filicaudatus, Aphelenchoides*
Add: *876 = Seinura filicaudata* Goodey, 1960

N—*wyganti*
　Plectonchus Massey, 1964 *1025a*

A—*xenoplax, Criconemoides*
　Add: *891 = Iota simile* Cobb, 1918
　1001a syn: *Hoplolaimus rusticus* of
　Stauffer, 1920 (p. 302) and
　Criconemoides rusticum of Taylor
　1936 (p. 412)

N—*xenura*
　Longidorella Khan & Siddiqi, 1963 *968*
　Enchodorella (Khan & Siddiqi, 1963)
　Siddiqi, 1964 *1090a*
　1090a syn: *Nordia thornei* Jairajpuri &
　Siddiqi, 1964

A—*xerokarterus, Aphelenchoides*
　Add: *Bursaphelenchus* (Rühm, 1956)
　Goodey, 1960 *876*

N—*xiphinemoides*
　Paralongidorus Heyns, 1965 *908a*

A—*xylebori, Tylenchus*
　Add: *Neoditylenchus* (Roux, 1906)
　Goodey, 1963 *881*

A—*xylophilus, Aphelenchoides*
　Add: NOTE: placed in *species inquiren-
　dae* by Goodey, 1960 *876*

A—*yanchiapingensis, Anguillulina*
　Add: NOTE: placed in *species inquiren-
　dae* by Andrássy, 1960 *761*

N—*yangambiensis*
　Dorylaimellus Geraert, 1962 *864*

A—*yucatanensis, Dorylaimus*
　Add: *Eudorylaimus* (Chitwood, 1938)
　Goodey, 1963 *881*

A—*zavadskii, Hoplolaimus*
　Add: *Criconemella* (Tulaganov, 1941)
　de Grisse & Loof, 1965 *891*

N—*zeae*
　Gymnotylenchus Siddiqi, 1961 *1075*

A—*zeae, Iotonchium*
　Add: NOTE: placed in *species inquiren-
　dae* by Meyl, 1961 *1028*

N—*zealandicus*
　Actinolaimus Clark, 1963 *825*

PAGE 159

A—*zealandicus, Tylencholaimus*
　Add: NOTE: placed in *species inquiren-
　dae* by Jairajpuri, 1965 *945*

A—*zeravschanicus, Aphelenchoides*
　Add: NOTE: placed in *species inquiren-
　dae* by Sanwal, 1961 *1060*

N—*zeylandicus*
　Mesodorylaimus Goodey, 1963 *881*
　881 syn: *Dorylaimus biroi,* var.
　zeylandicus Loos, 1945

A—*zimmermanni, Dorylaimus*
　NOTE: placed in *species inquirendae*
　by Jairajpuri, 1965 *945*

A—*zograffi, Dorylaimus*
　Add: NOTE: placed in *species inquiren-
　dae* by Meyl, 1961 *1028*

A—*zostericola, Tylenchus*
　Add: *Hirschmannia* (Allgén, 1934)
　Luc & Goodey, 1962 *1014*
　Hirschmanniella (Allgén, 1934) Luc
　& Goodey, 1964 *1015*
　NOTE: placed in *species inquirendae*
　by Luc & Goodey, 1962 *1014*

N—*zuckermani*
　Hemicycliophora Brzeski, 1963 *797*

N—*zulu*
　Xiphinema Heyns, 1965 *908*

A—*zurstrasseni, Diplogaster*
　Add: *Sachsia* (Sachs, 1950) Meyl,
　1961 *1028*
　Diplogasteritus (Sachs, 1950)
　Goodey, 1963 *881*

A,C—*zymosiphilus, Anguillula*
　1. Change species name to *zymosiphila*
　2. Place asterisk before *Anguillula*
　3. Add: *regarded as valid genus by
　Meyl, 1961 *1028*

List of References

Corrections to References in 1960 Check List

49d. Change last line to: Hungar 50(n.s. 9): 151-171.

183. Change date of authorship from 1912 to 1911; add to last line: (advanced separate 1911).

212. Change last line to: :: 878 pp., illus. Brill, Leiden.

218a. Change date of authorship from 1959 to 1960. Add (1959) immediately after 4(4).

286. Change date of authorship from 1942 to 1943. Add (1942) immediately after 20(1-2).

325b. Change date of authorship from 1959 to 1960. Add (1959) immediately after 4(4).

391ab. Change date of authorship from 1959 to 1960. Add (1959) immediately after 4(4).

481. On line 6, change München to Wien.

530. Delete brackets.

676b. Change first line to: Tanaka, I. and H. Tsumagari. 1954.

718. On line 5, change Movaya to Novaya.

720. On line 4, change Ied. An to Izdat. Akad. Nauk.

733ab, ac, and *ad.* Change date of authorship from 1959 to 1960. Add (1959) immediately after 4(4).

New References

[Brackets enclosing a date indicate a work not seen by the author. The symbol :: separates a title from the publishing information.]

750. Adams, R. E. and J. J. Eichenmuller. 1962.
Gracilacus capitatus n. sp. from scarlet oak in West Virginia. :: Nematologica 8(2): 87-92.

751. Akhtar, S. A. 1962.
Metaphelenchus sacchari n. sp. (Nematoda: Aphelenchoidea Fuchs 1937) associated with the roots of sugarcane. :: Nematologica 7(1): 53-56.

752. Akhtar, S. A. 1962.
Paracephalobus (Nematoda: Cephalobidae) a new genus of soil inhabiting nematodes. :: Proc. Helminth. Soc. Washington 29(2): 207-210.

753. Altherr, E. 1960.
Results from the Danish expedition to the French Cameroons (1949-1950). XXVIII—Nématodes limnicoles. :: Bull. l'I.F.A.N. 22, Ser. A, (3): 770-787.

754. Altherr, E. 1960.
Rhabditis guenini n. sp. :: Bull. Soc.
Vaudoise Sc. Nat. 67(301): 211-214.

755. Altherr, E. 1963.
Contribution à la connaissance de la
faune des sables submergés en Lorraine.
Nématodes. :: Ann. Spéléologie 18(1):
53-98.

756. Altherr, E. 1963
Nématodes d'eau douce. :: Etudes sur la
Faune du Sol, Biologie de L'Amérique
Australe, Vol. II, Paris, pp. 7-30.

757. Altherr, E. 1963.
Nématodes des sols forestiers subalpins
du Val Dischma (Grisons). :: Bull. Soc.
Vaudoise Sc. Nat. 68(312): 333-349.

757a. Altherr, E. 1965.
La faune des sables submergés des rives
du Rhin près de Krefeld. Nématodes. ::
Gewässer und Abwässer, Düsseldorf 1965
(39/40): 80-101.

758. Anderson, R. V. 1965.
Acrobeloides uberrinus n. sp., with a note
on morphologic variation within soil and
bacteria-reared populations. :: Proc.
Helminth. Soc. Washington 32(2): 232-
235.

759. Anderson, R. V. and W. J.
Bemrick. 1965.
Micronema deletrix n. sp., a saprophagous
nematode inhabiting a nasal tumor of a
horse. :: Proc. Helminth. Soc. Washington 32(1): 74-75.

760. Andrássy, I. 1959.
Nematoden aus dem Psammon des Adige-
Flusses, I. :: Mem. Mus. Civ. Stor. Nat.,
Verona 7: 163-181.

761. Andrássy, I. 1960.
Beiträge zur Kenntnis der freilebenden
Nematoden Chinas. :: Ann. Hist.-Nat.
Mus. Nat. Hungar. n.s. 52: 201-216.

762. Andrássy, I. 1960.
Einige Nematoden aus Afghanistan. ::
Opus Zool., Inst. Zoos. Univ. Budapest.
4(1) 3-14.

763. Andrássy, I. 1960.
Nematoden aus dem Periphyton der
Landungsmolen der Donau zwischen
Budapest und Mohács. :: Ann. Univ.
Scient. Budapest. Rolando Eötvös n.s.
Biol. 3: 3-21.

764. Andrássy, I. 1960
Panagrobelus topayi n. sp., eine neue
Nematoden-Art aus Kenya. :: Zool. Anz.,
Leipzig 164 (5-6): 195-198.

765. Andrássy, I. 1961.
Eine neue Art der seltenen Nematoden-
Gattung Triplonchium Cobb, 1920. ::
Nematologica 6(1): 37-41.

766. Andrássy, I. 1961.
Neue und seltene Arten der Familie
Alaimidae (Nematoda). :: Acta Zool.,
Acad. Scient. Hungar. 7(1-2): 1-18.

766a. Andrássy, I. 1961.
Wissenschaftliche Ergebnisse der ersten
ungarischen zoologischen Expedition in
Ostafrika. 2. Nematoda. :: Ann. Hist.-
Nat. Mus. Nat. Hungar. n.s. 53: 281-297.

767. Andrássy, I. 1961.
Zur Taxonomie der Neotylenchiden. ::
Nematologica 6(1): 25-36.

768. Andrássy, I. 1962.
Nematoden aus dem Psammon des Adige-
Flusses, II. :: Mem. Mus. Civ. Stor.
Nat., Verona 10:1-35.

769. Andrássy, I. 1962.
Nematoden aus dem Ufergrundwasser
der Donau von Bratislava bis Budapest
(Danubialia Hungarica, XVII). :: Arch.
Hydrobiol. Suppl. 27(1): 91-117.

769a. Andrássy, I. 1962.
Neue Nematoden-Arten aus Ungarn. 1.
Zehn neue Arten der Unterklasse Se-
cernentea (Phasmidia). :: Acta Zool.,
Acad. Scient. Hungar. 8(1-2): 1-23.

770. Andrássy, I. 1962.
Neue Nematoden-Arten aus Ungarn, II.
Fünf neue Arten der Überfamilie
Dorylaimoidea. :: Opus. Zool., Inst. Zoos.
Univ. Budapest. 4(2-4): 21-33.

771. Andrássy, I. 1962.
Zwei neue Nematoden-Arten aus dem Überschwemmungsgebiet der Donau (Danubialia Hungarica, XIII.). :: Opus. Zool., Inst. Zoos. Univ. Budapest 4(2-4): 3-8.

772. Andrássy, I. 1963.
Freilebende Nematoden aus Angola, I. Einige moosbewohnende Nematoden. :: Publ. Cult. Co. Diam. Ang. Lisboa. 66: 55-80.

773. Andrássy, I. 1963.
Nematologische Notizen, 12. :: Ann. Univ. Scient. Budapest. Rolando Eötvös n.s. Biol. 6: 3-12.

774. Andrássy, I. 1963.
The zoological results of Gy. Topál's collectings in South Argentina. 2. Nematoda—Neue und einige seltene Nematoden—Arten aus Argentinien. :: Ann. Hist.-Nat. Mus. Nat. Hungar. 55: 243-273.

775. Andrássy, I. 1964.
Dem Andenken Friedrich Paeslers. :: Opus. Zool., Inst. Zoos. Univ. Budapest. 5(1): 3-8.

776. Andrássy, I. 1964.
Einige Nematoden aus der Umgebung des Toten Meeres. :: Israel J. Zool. 13: 89-97.

777. Andrássy, I. 1964.
Ein Versuchsschlüssel zur Bestimmung der Tobrilus-Arten (Nematoda). :: Ann. Univ. Scient. Budapest. Rolando Eötvös n.s. Biol. 7: 3-18.

778. Andrássy, I. 1964.
Ergebnisse der zoologischen Forschungen von Dr. Z. Kaszab in der Mongolei. 4. Einige Bodennematoden aus der Mongolei. :: Ann. Hist.-Nat. Mus. Nat. Hungar. 56: 241-255.

779. Andrássy, I. 1964.
Neue Nematoden-Arten aus Ungarn, III. Fünf neue Arten. :: Opus. Zool., Inst. Zoos. Univ. Budapest. 5(1): 9-23.

780. Andrássy, I. 1964.
Onchulidae n. fam., eine neue Familie der Ordnung Enoplida (Nematoda). :: Opus. Zool., Inst. Zoos. Univ. Budapest. 5(1): 25-41.

781. Andrássy, I. 1964.
Süsswasser-Nematoden aus den Grossen Gebirgsgegenden Ostafrikas. :: Acta Zool., Acad. Scient. Hungar. 10(1-2): 1-59.

781a. Andrássy, I. 1965.
Erd- und Süsswasser-Nematoden aus Ghana Klasse Adenophorea (Aphasmidia). :: Opus. Zool., Inst. Zoos. Univ. Budapest. 5(2): 127-151.

781b. Andrássy, I. 1965.
Verzeichnis und Bestimmungsschlüssel der Arten der Nematoden-gattungen Criconemoides Taylor, 1936 und Mesocriconema n. gen. :: Opus. Zool., Inst. Zoos. Univ. Budapest. 5(2): 153-171.

782. Arias Delgado, M., F. Jiménez Millán and J. M. López Pedregal. 1965.
Tres nuevas especies de nematodes posibles fitoparásitos en suelos españoles. :: Publ. Inst. Biol. Apl. 38: 47-58.

783. Arias Delgado, M., J. M. López Pedregal and F. Jiménez Millán. 1963.
Nemátodes peri-radiculares en la vid. :: Bol. Real Soc. Española Hist. Nat., Sec. Biol. 61(1): 35-43.

784. Baker, A. D. 1962.
Check lists of the nematode superfamilies Dorylaimoidea, Rhabditoidea, Tylenchoidea, and Aphelenchoidea. :: E. J. Brill, Leiden, 261 pp.

785. Brizuela, R. B. 1963.
Hemicycliophora ritteri n. sp. (Nematoda: Criconematidae). :: Nematologica 9(1): 38-40.

786. Brzeski, M. W. 1960.
Cephalobus (Heterocephalobus) kaczanowskii subgen. nov., sp. nov. (Nematoda: Cephalobidae). :: Bull. Acad. Polon. Sci., Cl. II, 8(4): 163-165.

787. Brzeski, M. W. 1960.
Drei neue freilebende Nematoden aus Polen. :: Bull. Acad. Polon. Sci., Cl. II, 8(6): 261-264.

787a. Brzeski, M. W. 1961.
Altherrnema dibulbosa n.g., n. sp. (Nematoda, Panagrolaimidae). :: Bull. Acad. Polon. Sci., Cl. II, 9(8): 353-354.

788. Brzeski, M. W. 1961.
Revision of the genus Heterocephalus Brzeski, 1960, n. grad. (Nematoda: Cephalobidae). :: Bull. Acad. Polon. Sci., Cl. II, 9(2): 97-100.

789. Brzeski, M. W. 1961.
Two new species of free-living nematodes from Poland. :: Bull. Acad. Polon. Sci., Cl. II, 9(2): 91-95.

790. Brzeski, M. W. 1962.
A new nematode species Doryllium coronatum sp. n. from Poland (Nematoda, Leptonchidae). :: Bull. Acad. Polon. Sci., Cl. II, 10(7): 257-259.

791. Brzeski, M. W. 1962.
A rare nematode species, Aphelenchoides kungradensis Karimova, and a nomenclatorial note on A. spinocaudatus Skarbilovich (Nematoda, Aphelenchoididae). :: Bull. Acad. Polon. Sci., Cl. II, 10(11): 479-481.

792. Brzeski, M. W. 1962.
Eudorylaimus alleni n. sp. (Nematoda, Dorylaimidae). :: Opusc. Zool., Budapest 4(2-4): 67-68.

793. Brzeski, M. W. 1962.
Nematodes of peat-mosses of the Bialowieza Forest. :: Acta Zool. Cracov. 7(4): 53-62.

794. Brzeski, M. W. 1962.
Notes on the genus Aporcelaimus Thorne, Swanger (Nematoda, Dorylaimidae). :: Bull. Acad. Polon. Sci., Cl. II, 10(11): 469-472.

795. Brzeski, M. W. 1962.
Three new species of the genus Acrobeloides Cobb (Nematoda, Cephalobidae). :: Bull. Acad. Polon. Sci., Cl. II, 10(8): 335-339.

796. Brzeski, M. W. 1962.
Two new species of the genus Eudorylaimus Andrássy from Poland (Nematoda, Dorylaimidae). :: Bull. Acad. Polon. Sci., Cl. II, 10(12): 541-544.

797. Brzeski, M. W. 1963.
A new plant-parasitic nematode, Hemicycliophora zuckermani sp. n. (Nematoda, Criconematidae). :: Bull. Acad. Polon. Sci., Cl. II, 11(4): 173-176.

798. Brzeski, M. W. 1963.
Contribution to the knowledge of the Polish species of the genera Plectus Bastian and Anaplectus de Coninck et Sch. Stekh. (Nematoda, Plectidae) [Polish Text]. :: Frag. Faun., Warsawa 11(2): 21-30.

799. Brzeski, M. W. 1963.
Further studies on nematodes (Nematoda) of the Sphagnaceae of the Tatra Mountains [Polish Text]. :: Frag. Faun., Warsawa 10(21): 309-315.

800. Brzeski, M. W. 1963.
Nematode genera of the family Tripylidae (Nematoda, Enoplida). :: Acta Zool. Cracov. 8(7): 295-308.

801. Brzeski, M. W. 1963.
On the taxonomic status of Tylenchus filiformis Bütschli, 1873, and description of T. vulgaris sp. n. (Nematoda, Tylenchidae). :: Bull. Acad. Polon. Sci., Cl. II, 11: 531-535.

802. Brzeski, M. W. 1963.
Paratylenchus macrodorus n. sp. (Nematoda, Paratylenchidae), a new plant parasitic nematode from Poland. :: Bull. Acad. Polon. Sci., Cl. II, 11(6): 277-280.

803. Brzeski, M. W. 1963.
Review of the nematode genus Anaplectus de Coninck, Sch. Sth. (Nematoda, Plectidae). :: Bull. Acad. Polon. Sci., Cl. II, 11(1): 35-38.

804. Brzeski, M. W. 1963.
Tylenchus ditissimus sp. n., a new nematode from Poland (Nematoda, Tylenchidae). :: Bull. Acad. Polon. Sci., Cl. II, 11(11): 537-540.

805. Brzeski, M. W. 1964.
Einige neue und seltene Nematoden aus der Überfamilie *Dorylaimoidea* I. Unterfamilie *Dorylaiminae* (*Nematoda, Dorylaimidae*). :: Ann. Zool., Polska Akad. Nauk 22(1): 1-22.

806. Brzeski, M. W. 1964.
Revision der Gattungen *Tripyla* Bastian und *Paratripyla* gen. n. (*Nematoda, Tripylidae*). :: Ann. Zool., Polska Akad. Nauk 22(7): 157-178.

806a. Brzeski, M. W. [1964].
Stan badań faunistycznych i systematycznych nad wolnożyjącymi nicieniami Polski. :: Ekol. Polska, Ser. B, 10(1): 47-58.

807. Brzeski, M. W. 1965.
On the identity of *Trischistoma* Cobb and *Tripylina* Brzeski. :: Nematologica 11(3): 449.

808. Brzeski, M. W. and A. Szczygiel. 1961.
Two new species of the subfamily *Dorylaiminae* (*Nematoda, Dorylaimidae*). :: Bull. Acad. Polon. Sci., Cl. II, 9(12): 511-514.

809. Brzeski, M. W. and A. Szczygiel. 1964.
Studies on the nematodes of the genus *Paratylenchus* Micoletzky (Nematoda: Paratylenchinae) in Poland. Nematologica 9(4) (1963): 613-625.

810. Carvalho, J. C. 1959.
Descrição do macho de *Scutellonema boocki* (Nematoda: Tylenchidae). :: Arq. Inst. Biol. 26(6): 41-44.

811. Carvalho, J. C. 1959.
Helicotylenchus elisensis n. comb. (Nematoda: Tylenchidae). :: Arq. Inst. Biol. 26(7): 45-48.

811a. Carvalho, J. C. [1960].
Mononchus (*Cobbonchus*) *incultus*. :: Rev. Inst. Adolfo Lutz 20(1): 177-180.

811b. Carvalho, J. C. [1960].
Mononchus (*Iotonchus*) *piracicaboides* n. sp. :: Rev. Inst. Adolfo Lutz 20: 181-183.

812. Carvalho, J. C. 1962.
Xiphinema itanhaense n. sp. (*Nematoda: Dorylaimidae*) [Portuguese Text]. :: Arq. Inst. Biol. 29(26): 223-225.

813. Carvalho, J. C. 1965.
Xiphinema paulistanum—uma nova espécie de nematóide. :: Arq. Inst. Biol. 32(3): 77-79.

814. Clark, W. C. 1960.
New Zealand Mononchidae (Enoplida, Nematoda) 1. The genera *Mononchus* Bastian and *Prionchulus* Cobb. :: Nematologica 5(3): 199-214.

815. Clark, W. C. 1960.
Redescription of *Mononchus truncatus* Bastian, *M. papillatus* Bastian and *Prionchulus muscorum* (Dujardin) (Enoplida, Nematoda). :: Nematologica 5(3): 184-198.

815a. Clark, W. C. 1960.
The oesophago-intestinal junction in the Mononchidae (Enoplida, Nematoda). :: Nematologica 5(3): 178-183.

815b. Clark, W. C. 1961.
A revised classification of the order Enoplida (Nematoda). :: New Zealand J. Sci. 4(1): 123-150.

816. Clark, W. C. 1961.
The Mononchidae (Enoplida, Nematoda) of New Zealand II. The genus *Iotonchus* (Cobb, 1916) Altherr, 1950. :: Nematologica 5(4) (1960): 260-274.

817. Clark, W. C. 1961.
The Mononchidae (Enoplida: Nematoda) of New Zealand III. A review of the genus *Cobbonchus* Andrássy, 1958 with descriptions of new species. :: Nematologica 5(4) (1960): 275-284.

820. Clark, W. C. 1961.
The Mononchidae (Enoplida: Nematoda) of New Zealand IV. The genus *Mylonchulus* (Cobb, 1916) Pennak, 1953. :: Nematologica 6(1): 1-6.

821. Clark, W. C. 1962.
Amphorostoma saccatum n. gen. et sp. family Leptonchidae (Enoplida, Nematoda). :: Nematologica 7(3): 193-196.

822. Clark, W. C. 1963.
A new species of *Dolichodorus* (Nematoda: Tylenchida) from coastal dune sands. :: New Zealand J. Sci. 6(4): 531-534.

823. Clark, W. C. 1963.
A new species of *Longidorus* (Micol.) (Dorylaimida, Nematoda). :: New Zealand J. Sci. 6(4): 607-611.

824. Clark, W. C. 1963.
A new species of *Trichodorus* (Nematoda: Enoplida) from Westland, New Zealand. :: New Zealand J. Sci. 6(3): 414-417.

825. Clark, W. C. 1963.
New species of Dorylaimoid nematodes belonging to the genera *Pungentus* Thorne and Swanger, *Actinolaimus* Cobb and *Dorylaimellus* Cobb. :: New Zealand J. Sci. 6(4): 565-576.

826. Clark, W. C. 1963.
Notes on the Mononchidae (Nematoda) of the New Zealand region with descriptions of new species. :: New Zealand J. Sci. 6(4): 612-632.

827. Clark, W. C. 1964.
A new species of *Sectonema* Thorne, 1930 (Family Nygolaimidae, Nematoda). :: New Zealand J. Sci. 7(2): 174-176.

828. Clark, W. C. 1964.
Falcihasta palustris n. gen. et sp., family Belondiridae (Nematoda). :: New Zealand J. Sci. 7(2): 177-180.

829. Coetzee, Victoria. 1965.
South African species of the genus *Cobbonchus* Andrássy, 1958 (Nematoda: Mononchidae). :: Nematologica 11(2): 281-290.

830. Colbran, R. C. 1960.
Studies of plant and soil nematodes. 3. *Belonolaimus hastulatus, Psilenchus tumidus,* and *Hemicycliophora labiata,* three new species from Queensland. :: Queensland J. Agr. Sci. 17(3): 175-181.

830a. Colbran, R. C. 1961.
Studies of plant and soil nematodes. 4.

Tylenchulus obscurus n. sp. (Nematoda: Tylenchulidae). :: Queensland J. Agr. Sci. 18(2): 203-207.

831. Colbran, R. C. 1962.
Studies of plant and soil nematodes. 5. Four new species of Tylenchoidea from Queensland pineapple fields. :: Queensland J. Agr. Sci. 19(2): 231-239.

832. Colbran, R. C. 1963.
Studies of plant and soil nematodes. 6. Two new species from citrus orchards. :: Queensland J. Agr. Sci. 20(4): 469-474.

832a. Colbran, R. C. 1964.
Studies of plant and soil nematodes. 7. Queensland records of the order Tylenchida and the genera *Trichodorus* and *Xiphinema*. :: Queensland J. Agr. Sci. 21(1): 77-123.

832b. Colbran, R. C. 1965.
Studies of plant and soil nematodes. 8. Two new species of *Criconema* (Nematoda: Criconematidae) from Queensland. :: Queensland J. Agr. Anim. Sci. 22: 83-87.

832c. Colbran, R. C. 1965.
Studies of plant and soil nematodes. 9. *Trichodorus lobatus* n. sp. (Nematoda: Trichodoridae), a stubby-root nematode associated with citrus and peach trees. :: Queensland J. Agr. Anim. Sci. 22(3): 273-276.

832d. Colbran, R. C. 1965.
Studies of plant and soil nematodes. 10. *Paratylenchus coronatus* n. sp. (Nematoda: Criconematidae), a pin nematode associated with citrus. :: Queensland J. Agr. Anim. Sci. 22(3): 277-279.

833. de Coninck, L. 1962.
Bijdragen tot de kennis der plantenparasitaire en der vrijlevende nematoden van Kongo (Contributions à la connaissance des nématodes phytoparasites et libres du Congo). IV- Nématodes associés à des cotonniers "wiltés." :: Inst. Dierk., Lab. Syst., Rijksuniv. Gent: 3-13.

834. Coomans, A. 1962.
Some species of Dorylaimoidea found in Belgium. I. Members of the Tylencholaiminae Filipjev, 1934. :: Nematologica 7(2): 146-154.

835. Coomans, A. 1962.
Systematisch-ecologisch onderzoek van de vrijlevende Bodemnematoden in België. De vrijlevende nematoden-fauna van weideland, I. :: Natuurwet. Tijdschr. 43(1961): 87-132.

836. Coomans, A. 1965.
Xiphinema basilgoodeyi n. sp. with observations on its larval stages (Nematoda: Dorylaimina). :: Nematologica 10(4) (1964): 581-593.

837. Coomans, A. and E. Geraert. 1962.
Some species of Dorylaimoidea found in Belgium. II. Monodelphic Dorylaiminae. :: Nematologica 8(3): 233-241.

838. Coomans, A. and J. B. Goodey. 1965.
Drilocephalobus congoensis n.g., n. sp. :: Nematologica 11(1): 116-120.

839. Coomans, A. and M. B. Lima. 1965.
Description of *Anatonchus amiciae* n. sp. (Nematoda: Mononchidae) with observations on its juvenile stages and anatomy. :: Nematologica 11(3): 413-431.

840. Corbett, D. C. M. 1964.
I. *Ecphyadophora quadralata* n. sp. and two species of *Ecphyadophoroides* n. gen. (Nematoda: Neotylenchidae). :: Nematologica 10(1): 121-130.

841. Corbett, D. C. M. 1964.
Longidorus utriculoides n. sp. (Nematoda: Dorylaimidae) from Nyasaland. :: Nematologica 10(3): 496-499.

842. Das, V. M. 1960.
Studies on the nematode parasites of plants in Hyderabad (Andhra Pradesh, India). :: Ztschr. Parasitenk. 19: 553-605.

843. Das, V. M. 1962.
Studies on the morphology of female Eudorylaimus obscurus (Thorne and Swanger, 1936) Andrássy 1959. :: Canad. J. Zool. 40: 747-754.

844. Das, V. M. 1964.
Hexatylus mulveyi n. sp. and Deladenus durus (Cobb, 1922) Thorne, 1941 (Nematoda: Neotylenchidae) from the Canadian Arctic. :: Canad. J. Zool. 42: 649-653.

845. Diab, K. A. and W. R. Jenkins. 1965.
Description of *Neocriconema adamsi* n. gen., n. sp. (Criconematidae: Nematoda) with a key to the species of *Neocriconema*. :: Proc. Helminth. Soc. Washington 32(2): 193-197.

846. Di Edwardo, A. A. and V. G. Perry. 1964.
Heterodera leuceilyma n. sp. (Nemata: Heteroderidae), a severe pathogen of St. Augustine grass in Florida. :: Fla. Agr. Exp. Sta. Bull. 687, 35 pp.

847. Edward, J. C. and S. L. Misra. 1963.
Criconema mangiferum n. sp. associated with roots of mango in India. :: Nematologica 9(2): 222-224.

848. Edward, J. C. and S. L. Misra. 1963.
Criconemoides nainitalense n. sp. (Nematoda: Criconematidae). :: Nematologica 9(2): 218-221.

849. Edward, J. C. and S. L. Misra. 1963.
Paratylenchus nainianus n. sp. (Nematoda: Criconematidae) from Uttar Pradesh, India. :: Nematologica 9(2): 215-217.

850. Edward, J. C. and S. L. Misra. 1964.
Criconemoides magnoliae n. sp. and *C. juniperi* n. sp. (Nematoda: Criconematidae) from Kumaon region, Uttar Pradesh, India. :: Nematologica 10(1): 95-100.

References 851 – 864

851. Edward, J. C. and S. L. Misra. 1964.
Hemicriconemoides communis n. sp. and *H. litchi* n. sp. (Nematoda: Criconematidae), from Uttar Pradesh, India. :: Nematologica 9(3) (1963): 405-411.

852. Edward, J. C., S. L. Misra and G. R. Singh. 1965.
Hemicriconemoides birchfieldi n. sp. (Nematoda: Criconematidae) from Allahabad, Uttar Pradesh, India; with a revision of the key to species of *Hemicriconemoides*. :: Nematologica 11(2): 157-161.

852a. Erzhanov, P. K. [1964].
Nine new nematode species [Russian Text]. :: Trudy Karakalpaksk. Gos. Ped. In-t. 2: 175-185.

853. Esser, R. P. 1960.
Three additional species in the genus *Hemicriconemoides* Chitwood and Birchfield 1957 (Nemata: Tylenchida). :: Nematologica 5(1): 64-71.

854. Ferris, Virginia R. 1961.
A new species of *Pratylenchus* (Nemata-Tylenchida) from roots of soybeans. :: Proc. Helminth. Soc. Washington 28(2): 109-111.

855. Ferris, Virginia R. 1963.
Tylenchorhynchus silvaticus n. sp. and *Tylenchorhynchus agri* n. sp. (Nematoda: Tylenchida). :: Proc. Helminth. Soc. Washington 30(2): 165-168.

856. Fisher, J. M. 1964.
Dolichodorus adelaidensis n. sp. and *Paralongidorus eucalypti* n. sp. from S. Australia. :: Nematologica 10(3): 464-470.

857. Fisher, J. M. 1965.
Studies on *Paratylenchus nanus* I. Effects of variation in environment on several morphometric characters of adults. :: Nematologica 11(2): 269-279.

858. Fisher, J. M. 1965.
Telotylenchus whitei n. sp. from S. Australia with observations on *Telotylenchus hastulatus* (Colbran 1960) n. comb. :: Nematologica 10(4) (1964): 563-569.

859. Flores-Barroeta, L. and E. Hidalgo-Escalante. 1961.
Estudios fitonematologices de suelos Mexicanos. I. :: Rev. Iberica Parasit. 21(2): 221-237.

860. Franklin, Mary T. 1961.
A British root-knot nematode, *Meloidogyne artiellia* n. sp. :: J. Helminth. (R. T. Leiper Supp.): 85-92.

861. Franklin, Mary T. 1965.
A root-knot nematode, *Meloidogyne naasi* n. sp., on field crops in England and Wales. :: Nematologica 11(1): 79-86.

862. Franklin, Mary T. and D. J. Hooper. 1962.
Bursaphelenchus fungivorus n. sp. (Nematoda: Aphelenchoidea) from rotting gardenia buds infected with *Botrytis cinerea* Pers. ex. Fr. :: Nematologica 8(2): 136-142.

863. Franklin, Mary T. and M. R. Siddiqi. 1963.
Aphelenchoides trivialis n. sp. from South India. :: Nematologica 9(1): 15-18.

863a. Furstenberg, J. P. and J. Heyns. 1965.
Two new species of the genus *Discolaimium* Thorne 1939 (Nematoda: Dorylaimoidea) from South Africa. :: South African J. Agr. Sci. 8: 1155-1159.

864. Geraert, E. 1962.
Bijdragen tot de kennis der plantenparasitaire en der vrijlevende nematoden van Kongo (Contributions à la connaissance des nematodes phytoparasites et libres du Congo). II.- De Nematodenfauna in en om de wortels van *Musa parasidiaca normalis* (La Faune Nématologique dans les racines de *Musa parasidiaca normalis* et dans le sol environnant) [with English summary]. :: Inst. Dierk., Lab. Syst., Rijksuniv. Gent: 5-73.

865. Geraert, E. 1962.
Bijdragen tot de kennis der plantenparasitaire en der vrijlevende nematoden van Kongo (Contributions à la connaissance des nematodes phytoparasites et libres du Congo). V.- Two new species of the Dorylaiminae. :: Inst. Dierk., Lab. Syst., Rijksuniv. Gent: 3-19.

866. Geraert, E. 1965.
The genus *Paratylenchus*. :: Nematologica 11(3): 301-334.

867. Geraert, E. and J. B. Goodey. 1964.
The priority of *Tylenchus hexalineatus* over *T. megacephalus*. :: Nematologica 9(3) (1963): 471.

868. Gerlach, S. A. 1954.
Brasilianische Meeres-Nematoden 1. :: Bol. Inst. Oceanog. 5(1-2): 3-69.

869. Gillespie, W. H. and R. E. Adams. 1962.
An awl nematode, *Dolichodorus silvestris* n. sp. from West Virginia. :: Nematologica 8(2): 93-98.

870. Golden, A. M. 1961.
Paratylenchus steineri (Criconematidae) a new species of plant nematode. :: Proc. Helminth. Soc. Washington 28(1): 9-11.

871. Golden, A. M. and W. Birchfield. 1965.
Meloidogyne graminicola (Heteroderidae) a new species of root-knot nematode from grass. :: Proc. Helminth. Soc. Washington 32(2): 228-231.

872. Golden, A. M. and Grace S. Cobb. 1963.
Heterodera lespedezae (Heteroderidae), a new species of cyst-forming nematode. :: Proc. Helminth. Soc. Washington 30(2): 281-286.

873. Golden, A. M. and W. Friedman. 1964.
Some taxonomic studies on the genus *Criconema* (Nematoda: Criconematidae). :: Proc. Helminth. Soc. Washington 31(1): 47-59.

874. Golden, A. M., G. J. Rau and Grace S. Cobb. 1962.
Heterodera cyperi (Heteroderidae), a new species of cyst-forming nematode. :: Proc. Helminth. Soc. Washington 29(2): 168-173.

875. Goodey, J. B. 1960.
Rhadinaphelenchus cocophilus (Cobb, 1919) n. comb., the nematode associated with "red-ring" disease of coconut. :: Nematologica 5(2): 98-102.

876. Goodey, J. B. 1960.
The classification of the Aphelenchoidea Fuchs, 1937. :: Nematologica 5(2): 111-126.

877. Goodey, J. B. 1961.
The nature of the spear guiding apparatus in Dorylaimidae. :: J. Helminth. (R. T. Leiper Supp.): 101-106.

878. Goodey, J. B. 1962.
Tylenchus (*Cephalenchus*) *megacephalus* n. sbg., n. sp. :: Nematologica 7(4): 331-333.

879. Goodey, J. B. and D. J. Hooper. 1965.
A neotype of *Aphelenchus avenae* Bastian, 1865 and the rejection of *Metaphelenchus* Steiner, 1943. :: Nematologica 11(1): 55-65.

880. Goodey, J. B. and J. W. Seinhorst. 1960.
Further observations and comments on the identity of *Rotylenchus robustus* (de Man, 1876) Filipjev, 1934 with a description of a proposed neotype and a new definition of *Rotylenchus goodeyi*. :: Nematologica 5(2): 136-148.

881. Goodey, T. 1963.
Soil and freshwater nematodes. :: London: Methuen. 2nd ed. revised by J. B. Goodey. 544 pp.

882. Grandison, G. S. 1964.
A new species of *Doryllium* (Nematoda: Dorylaimida) from Auckland and Campbell Islands. :: New Zealand J. Agr. Res. 7(2): 169-173.

883. de Grisse, A. 1961.
Meloidogyne kikuyensis n. sp., a para-site of Kikuyu grass (*Pennisetum clan-destinum*) in Kenya. :: Nematologica 5(4) (1960): 303-308.

884. de Grisse, A. 1962.
Paratylenchus vandenbrandei, n. sp. (Nematoda-Criconematidae) nouvelle espèce de *Paratylenchus,* associée aux racines d'agave au Kenya. :: Nemato-logica 8(3): 229-232.

885. de Grisse, A. 1963.
Criconemoides deconincki n. sp., (Nem-atoda). :: Meded. Landb. Opzoek. Staat Gent 28(3): 611-617.

886. de Grisse, A. 1964.
Criconema microdorum n. sp. (Nema-toda: Criconematidae). :: Nematologica 10(1): 164-167.

887. de Grisse, A. 1964.
Criconemoides flandriensis n. sp. (Nem-atoda: Criconematidae). :: Nematolo-gica 9(4) (1963): 547-552.

888. de Grisse, A. 1964.
Hemicriconemoides pseudobrachyurum n. sp. (Nematoda: Criconematidae). :: Nematologica 10(3): 369-372.

889. de Grisse, A. 1964.
Morphological observations on Cricone-moides, with a description of four new species found in Belgium (Nematoda). :: Meded. Landb. Opzoek. Staat Gent 29(3): 734-761.

890. de Grisse, A. and H. Koen. 1964.
Criconemoides pseudohercyniensis n. sp. (Nematoda: Criconematidae). :: Nem-atologica 10(2): 197-200.

891. de Grisse, A. and P. A. A. Loof. 1965.
Revision of the genus Criconemoides (Nematoda). :: Meded. Landb. Op-zoek. Staat Gent 30(2): 577-603.

892. de Guiran, G. 1963.
Quatre espèces nouvelles du genre *Criconemoides* (Taylor) (*Nematoda-Criconematidae*). :: Rev. Path. Veg. Ent. Agr. France 42(1): 1-11.

893. de Guiran, G. 1963.
Un nématode nouveau associé aux cul-tures l'agrumes au Maroc. :: Compt. Rend. Acad. Agr. France 49: 392-394.

894. de Guiran, G. 1964.
Mesotylus: Nouveau genre de Pratylen-chinae (Nematoda: Tylenchoidea). :: Nematolgica 9(4) (1963): 567-575.

895. Hechler, Helen C. 1962.
The description, feeding habits, and life history of *Neotylenchus lindfordi* n. sp.; a mycophagous nematode. :: Proc. Hel-minth. Soc. Washington 29(1): 19-27.

896. Hechler, Helen C. 1963.
Description, developmental biology, and feeding habits of *Seinura tenuicaudata* (de Man) J. B. Goodey, 1960 (Nema-toda: Aphelenchoididae), a nematode predator. :: Proc. Helminth. Soc. Wash-ington 30(2): 182-195.

897. Hechler, Helen C. and D. P. Taylor. 1965.
Taxonomy of the genus *Seinura* (Nema-toda: Aphelenchoididae), with descrip-tions of S. *celeris* n. sp. and S. *steineri* n. sp. :: Proc. Helminth. Soc. Washing-ton 32(2): 205-219.

898. Heyns, J. 1962.
A report on South African nematodes of the families Longidoridae, Belondiridae and Alaimidae (Nemata: Dorylaimoi-dea), with descriptions of three new species. :: Nematologica 8(1): 15-20.

899. Heyns, J. 1962.
Elaphonema mirabile n. gen., n. sp. (Rhabditida), a remarkable new mem-atode [sic] from South Africa. :: Proc. Helminth. Soc. Washington 29(2): 128-130.

900. Heyns, J. 1962.
Osstella hamata n. gen., n. sp., *Zeldia serrata* n. sp. and *Acrobeles thornei* n. sp., three new nematodes from South Africa (Rhabditida: Cephalobidae). :: Nematologica 8(4): 301-306.

901. Heyns, J. 1962.
Two new species of Criconematidae from South Africa. :: Nematologica 8(1): 21-24.

902. Heyns, J. 1963.
A report on South African nematodes of the genera *Labronema* Thorne, *Discolaimus* Cobb, *Discolaimoides* n. gen., and *Discolaimium* Thorne (Nemata: Dorylaimoidea). :: Proc. Helminth. Soc. Washington 30(1): 1-6.

903. Heyns, J. 1963.
Five new species of Leptonchidae (Nemata: Dorylaimoidea) from South Africa. :: Proc. Helminth. Soc. Washington 30(1): 7-15.

904. Heyns, J. 1963.
New species of the superfamily *Dorylaimoidea* (Nemata) from South African soils, with a description of a new genus *Kochinema*. :: South African J. Agr. Sci. 6: 289-302.

905. Heyns, J. 1964.
Aphelenchoides helicus n. sp. and *Ditylenchus equalis* n. sp., two new soil-inhabiting nematodes. :: South African J. Agr. Sci. 7: 147-150.

906. Heyns, J. 1964.
Notes on the genus *Dorylaimellus* Cobb, 1913 (Nemata: Dorylaimoidea), with descriptions of four new species. :: Nematologica 9(3) (1963): 391-404.

907. Heyns, J. 1964.
Vanderlindia duplopapillata n. gen., n. sp. (Nematoda: Dorylaimoidea), with a note on certain organs in the oesophageal region. :: Nematologica 10(2): 301-305.

908. Heyns, J. 1965.
Four new species of the genus *Xiphinema* (Nematoda: Dorylaimoidea) from South Africa. :: Nematologica 11(1): 87-99.

908a. Heyns, J. 1965.
New species of the genera *Paralongidorus* and *Longidorus* (Nematoda: Dorylaimoidea) from South Africa. :: South African J. Agr. Sci. 8: 863-874.

908b. Heyns, J. and Gerda Lagerwey. 1965.
Nematodes of the superfamily Dorylaimoidea collected in the northern part of the Kruger National Park. :: Koedoe 8: 129-135.

908c. Heyns, J. and Gerda Lagerwey. 1965.
South African species of the genus *Iotonchus* Cobb, 1916 (Nematoda: Mononchidae). :: South African J. Agr. Sci. 8: 775-784.

909. Hooper, D. J. 1961.
A redescription of *Longidorus elongatus* (de Man, 1876) Thorne & Swanger, 1936, (Nematoda, Dorylaimidae) and descriptions of five new species of *Longidorus* from Great Britain. :: Nematologica 6(3): 237-257.

910. Hooper, D. J. 1962.
Three new species of *Trichodorus* (Nematoda: Dorylaimoidea) and observations of *T. minor* Colbran, 1956. :: Nematologica 7(4): 273-280.

911. Hooper, D. J. 1963.
Trichodorus viruliferus n. sp. (Nematoda: Dorylaimida). :: Nematologica 9(2): 200-204.

912. Hooper, D. J., K. Kuiper and P. A. A. Loof. 1964.
Observations on the identity of *Trichodorus teres* Hooper, 1962 and *T. flevensis* Kuiper & Loof, 1962. :: Nematologica 9(4) (1963): 646.

913. Hopper, B. E. 1960.
Contributions to the knowledge of the genus Meloidodera (Nematoda: Tylenchida), with a description of M. charis n. sp. :: Canad. J. Zool. 38(5): 939-947.

914. Hopper, B. E. 1961.
Swangeria bisexualis n. sp. (Belondiridae: Nematoda) from Florida. :: Canad. J. Zool. 39: 69-72.

914a. Hopper, B. E. 1963.
The males of Criconema menzeli (Stefański, 1924) Taylor, 1936 and C. octangulare (Cobb, 1914) Taylor, 1936 (Criconematidae: Tylenchida). :: Canad. J. Zool., 41: 595-597.

915. Husain, S. I. and A. M. Khan. 1965.
A new genus and six new species of nematodes from India belonging in the family Neotylenchidae with an amendation of the subfamily Ecphyadophorinae. :: Proc. Helminth. Soc. Washington 32(1): 7-15.

916. Husain, S. I. and A. M. Khan. 1965.
A new genus and two new species of nematodes from India belonging to the family Dorylaimidae with an amendation of the subfamily Nordianae. :: Proc. Helminth. Soc. Washington 32(1): 49-52.

917. Husain, S. I. and A. M. Khan. 1965.
On *Rotylenchulus stakmani* n. sp. with a key to the species of the genus (Nematoda: Tylenchida). :: Proc. Helminth. Soc. Washington 32(1): 21-23.

918. Husain, S. I. and A. M. Khan. 1965.
Seinura nagini n. sp. (Nematoda: Aphelenchoididae) from North India. :: Proc. Helminth. Soc. Washington 32(2): 179-181.

919. Husain, S. I. and A. M. Khan. 1965.
Two new species of *Boleodorus* Thorne, 1941 (Nematoda: Neotylenchidae) from India. :: Proc. Helminth. Soc. Washington 32(2): 176-179.

920. Husain, S. I. and A. M. Khan. 1965.
Tylencholaimellus thornei n. sp. (Dorylaimoidea: Leptonchidae) from India. :: Proc. Helminth. Soc. Washington 32(1): 75-77.

921. Husain, S. I., A. M. Khan, and J. J. s'Jacob. 1965.
Four new species of *Diphtherophora* de Man, 1880 (Nematoda: Diphtherophoridae) with a key to the species of the genus. :: Proc. Helminth. Soc. Washington 32(2): 186-191.

922. Inglis, W. G. and J. W. Coles. 1961.
The species of *Rhabditis* (Nematoda) found in rotting seaweed on British beaches. :: Bull. British Mus. (Nat. Hist.) Zool. 7(6): 320-333.

923. Ivanova, T. S. 1958.
Soil nematodes of the genus Diphtherophora in the U.S.S.R. [Russian Text]. :: Summaries of Communications, Sci. Conf. All-union Soc. Helminth. 4: 55-56.

924. Ivanova, A. I. 1960.
Peplorhabditis vestibularis n. g., n. sp. (Nematodes, Rhabditidae)—living in rotting cucumbers in the Stalingrad region [Russian Text]. :: Nauk. Doklady Vyss. Skoly. Biol. Nauk 3: 7-9.

925. s'Jacob, J. J. and P. A. A. Loof. 1962.
The taxonomic status of the genera *Bathyodontus* Fielding, 1950 and *Mirolaimus* Andrássy, 1956. :: Nematologica 8(1): 66-74.

926. Jairajpuri, M. S. 1962.
On a new nematode *Boleodorus indicus* n. sp. (Neotylenchidae: Tylenchida), from soil about the roots of onions, *Allium cepa* L. :: Ztschr. Parasitenk. 22(3): 214-216.

927. Jairajpuri, M. S. 1963.
Criconema simlaensis n. sp. (Nematoda: Criconematidae) from India. :: Ztschr. Parasitenk. 23(3): 235-238.

928. Jairajpuri, M. S. 1963.
On the status of the subfamilies Rotylenchoidinae Whitehead, 1958, and Telotylenchinae Siddiqi, 1960. :: Ztschr. Parasitenk. 23: 320-323.

References 929 – 944

929. Jairajpuri, M. S. 1964. *Criconema taylori* n. sp. (Nematoda: Criconematidae) from South India. :: Nematologica 10(1): 108-110.

930. Jairajpuri, M. S. 1964 *Criconemoides basili* nom. nov. (syn. *Criconemoides goodeyi* Jairajpuri, 1963 preoccupied). :: Nematologica 10(1): 183.

931. Jairajpuri, M. S. 1964. *Dorella mira* n. gen., n. sp., (Nematoda: Dorylaimoidea) from India. :: Proc. Helminth. Soc. Washington 31(2): 222-224.

932. Jairajpuri, M. S. 1964. *Doryllium minor* n. sp. (Nematoda: Dorylaimoidea) from North India. :: Nematologica 9(4) (1963) 602-604.

933. Jairajpuri, M. S. 1964. *Leptonema thornei* n. gen., n. sp. (Nematoda: Dorylaimoidea) from India. :: Nematologica 10(3): 399-402.

934. Jairajpuri, M. S. 1964. *Rotylenchus sheri* n. sp. (Nematoda: Tylenchida) from North India. :: Nematologica 9(3) (1963): 378-380.

935. Jairajpuri, M. S. 1964. Studies on Campydoridae and Leptonchidae (Nematoda: Dorylaimoidea) with description of *Basirotyleptus basiri* n. gen., n. sp., from India. :: Proc. Helminth. Soc. Washington 31(1): 59-64.

936. Jairajpuri, M. S. 1964. Studies on Nygellidae n. fam. and Belondiridae Thorne, 1939 (Nematoda: Dorylaimoidea) with description of ten new species from India. :: Proc. Helminth. Soc. Washington 31(2): 173-187.

937. Jairajpuri, M. S. 1964. Studies on the genus *Proleptonchus* Lordello, 1955 (Dorylaimoidea: Leptonchidae) with description of two new species from India. :: Nematologica 10(1): 116-120.

938. Jairajpuri, M. S. 1964. Two new species of the genus *Criconemoides* Taylor, 1936 (Nematoda: Criconematidae) from North India. :: Nematologica 9(3) (1963): 381-385.

938a. Jairajpuri, M. S. [1965]. A new species of the nematode genus *Axonchium* Cobb, with notes on the occurrence of *A. caudatum* Williams in India, and the taxonomic status of *Discolaimium pakistanicum* Timm and Bhuiyan. :: Proc. Zool. Soc., Calcutta 18(2): 155-158.

939. Jairajpuri, M. S. 1965. *Basiria kashmirensis* n. sp. (Nematoda: Tylenchida) from India. :: Labdev J. Sci. Tech., India 3(1): 23-25.

940. Jairajpuri, M. S. 1965. *Oostenbrinkella oostenbrinki* n. gen., n. sp. (Nematoda: Leptonchidae) from the soil around the roots of the jacktree. :: Proc. Helminth. Soc. Washington 32(2): 122-124.

941. Jairajpuri, M. S. 1965. *Qudsianema amabilis* n. gen., n. sp. (Nematoda: Dorylaimoidea) from India. :: Proc. Helminth. Soc. Washington 32(1): 72-73.

942. Jairajpuri, M. S. 1965. Studies on *Dorylaimellus* Cobb, 1913 and *Nygellus* Thorne, 1939 (Nematoda: Dorylaimoidea) with descriptions of three new species. :: Nematologica 11(2): 207-212.

943. Jairajpuri, M. S. 1965. Studies on the genus *Lordellonema* Andrássy (Ncmatoda: Dorylaimoidea) with description of *Lordellonema warriari* n. sp. from India. :: Proc. Helminth. Soc. Washington 32(1): 99-102.

944. Jairajpuri, M. S. 1965. Three new species of Dorylaimoidea (Nematoda) from India. :: Proc. Helminth. Soc. Washington 32(1): 78-81.

945. Jairajpuri, M. S. 1965.
Three new species of the genus *Tylencholaimus* de Man, 1876 (Nematoda: Dorylaimoidea) from India. :: Nematologica 10(4) (1964): 512-518.

946. Jairajpuri, M. S. and A. H. Siddiqi. 1963.
A new and known species of the genus *Tylencholaimellus* M. V. Cobb, 1915 (Nematoda: Dorylaimoidea) from India with a key to its species. :: Ztschr. Parasitenk. 22: 489-494.

947. Jairajpuri, M. S. and A. H. Siddiqi. 1963.
On *Psilenchus neoformis* n. sp. (Nematoda: Tylenchida) from Solon (H.P.), North India. :: Current Sci. Bangalore 32: 318-319.

948. Jairajpuri, M. S. and A. H. Siddiqi. 1963.
On three new species of the genus *Criconemoides* Taylor, 1936 (Nematoda: Criconematidae) from North India. :: Ztschr. Parasitenk. 23: 340-347.

949. Jairajpuri, M. S. and A. H. Siddiqi. 1963.
Xiphinema brevicolle Lordello and Da Costa, 1961: (Nematoda: Dorylaimoidea) from Dalhousie (H.P.), North India. :: Current Sci. Bangalore 32(11): 508.

950. Jairajpuri, M. S. and A. H. Siddiqi. 1964.
On a new nematode genus *Nordia* (Dorylaimoidea: Nordianae n. subfam.) with remarks on the genus *Longidorella* Thorne, 1939. :: Proc. Helminth. Soc. Washington 31(1): 1-9.

951. Jenkins, W. R. 1960.
Paratylenchus marylandicus, n. sp. (Nematoda: Criconematidae) associated with roots of pine. :: Nematologica 5(3): 175-177.

952. Jenkins, W. R. and J. P. Reed. 1964.
Two new species of *Hemicycliophora* (Nematoda: Criconematidae) with a note on *Hemicycliophora ritteri.* :: Nematologica 10(1): 111-115.

953. Jensen, H. J. 1963.
Trichodorus allius, a new species of stubby-root nematode from Oregon (Nemata: Dorylaimoidea). :: Proc. Helminth. Soc. Washington 30(1): 157-159.

954. Jiménez-Millán, F., M. Arias Delgado and M. A. Fijo. 1964.
Aorolaimus capsici n. sp. (Nematoda, Hoplolaiminae). :: Bol. Real Soc. Española Hist. Nat., Sec. Biol. 62: 283-287.

954a. Kakulija, G. A. and S. L. Lazarevskaja. [1965].
Ektaphelenchus piniperdae nov. sp. (*Tylenchida, Aphelenchoididae*)–new nematode from *Blastophagus piniperda* [Russian Text]. :: Proc. Helm. Lab. Acad. Sci. USSR 15: 84-85.

955. Kannan, S. 1960.
Soil nematodes from Madras City. :: J. Zool. Soc. India 12(1): 40-50.

956. Kannan, S. 1961.
Further additions to the list of *Mononchus* from Madras City. :: J. Madras Univ. B. 31(1): 59-62.

957. Kannan, S. 1961.
Nematodes of the genus *Mononchus* from Madras City. :: J. Madras Univ. B. 31(1): 69-74.

958. Kannan, S. 1961.
Soil nematodes of Madras City-II. :: J. Zool. Soc. India 13(1): 56-61.

959. Kannan, S. 1961.
Soil nematodes of the genera *Mononchus* and *Mononchulus*. :: J. Madras Univ. B. 31(1): 63-68.

959a. Khan, A. M. and S. I. Husain. 1965.
Heterodera mothi n. sp. (Tylenchida: Heteroderidae) parasitising *Cyperus rotundus* L. at Aligarh, U.P., India. :: Nematologica 11(2): 167-172.

960. Khan, E. 1964.
Boleodorus mirus n. sp. (Tylenchida: Boleodorinae n. subfam.) from Kufri, Simla (H.P.) India, with a key to the species of the genus *Boleodorus* Thorne, 1941. :: Zool. Anz., Leipzig 173(5): 336-341.

961. Khan, E. 1964.
Enchodorella, a new nematode genus in the family Dorylaimidae with description of E. perveeni n. sp. :: Labdev J. Sci. Tech., India 2(1): 49-51.

962. Khan, E. 1964.
Longidorus afzali n. sp., and *Xiphinema arcum* n. sp. (Nematoda: Longidoridae) from India. :: Nematologica 10(2): 313-318.

963. Khan, E. and M. A. Basir. 1963.
Boleodorus similis n. sp. (Nematoda, Nothotylenchinae) from India. :: Ztschr. Parasitenk. 23(2): 121-123.

964. Khan, E. and M. A. Basir. 1963.
Two new species of the genus *Hemicycliophora* de Man, 1921 (Nematoda: Criconematidae) from North India. :: Nematologica 9(1): 101-105.

965. Khan, E. and M. A. Basir. 1964.
Boleodorus impar n. sp. (Nematoda: Tylenchida) from India. :: Proc. Helminth. Soc. Washington 31(2): 187-190.

966. Khan, E. and S. H. Khan. 1964.
Longidorella impar n. sp. (Nematoda: Longidorinae) from North India. :: Zool. Anz., Leipzig 173(5): 345-347.

967. Khan, E. and M. R. Siddiqi. 1963.
Criconema serratum n. sp. (Nematoda: Criconematidae), a parasite of peach trees in Almora, North India. :: Current Sci. Bangalore 32: 414-415.

968. Khan, E. and M. R. Siddiqi. 1963.
Longidorella xenura n. sp. (Nematoda: Dorylaimoidea) found around apricot roots in Almora, North India. :: Current Sci. Bangalore 32: 363-364.

969. Khan, E. and M. R. Siddiqi. 1964.
Criconema laterale n. sp. (Nematoda: Criconematidae) from Srinagar, Kashmir. :: Nematologica 9(4) (1963): 584-586.

970. Khan, M. A. 1957.
Sphaerularia bombi Duf. (Nematoda: Allantonematidae) infesting bumblebees and Sphaerularia hastata sp. nov. infesting bark beetles in Canada. :: Canad. J. Zool. 35: 519-523.

971. Khan, M. A. 1957.
Sphaerularia ungulacauda sp. nov. (Nematoda: Allantonematidae) from the Douglas Fir beetle, Dendroctonus pseudotsugae Hopk., with key to Sphaerularia species (emended). :: Canad. J. Zool. 35: 635-639.

972. Khan, M. A. 1960.
Descriptions of two nematodes, Ektaphelenchus macrostylus n. sp., and Laimaphelenchus ulmi n. sp., with a key to the species of Laimaphelenchus. :: Canad. J. Zool. 38: 91-97.

973. Khan, M. A. 1960.
Stictylus hastatus (Khan, 1957) n. comb. and Stictylus ungulacaudus (Khan, 1957) n. comb. (Nematoda: Neotylenchidae). :: Canad. J. Zool. 38: 225-226.

975. Khan, S. H. 1964.
Criconemoides siddiqii n. sp. (Nematoda: Criconematidae) from North India. :: Zool. Anz., Leipzig 173(5): 342-344.

976. Khan, S. H. 1965.
Nothotylenchus acutus n. sp. and *N. basiri* n. sp. (Nematoda: Nothotylenchinae) from North India. :: Proc. Helminth. Soc. Washington 32(1): 90-93.

977. Khan, S. H. and M. A. Basir. 1964.
Two new species of the genus *Helicotylenchus* Steiner, 1945, (Nematoda: Hoplolaimidae) from India. :: Proc. Helminth. Soc. Washington 31(2): 199-202.

978. Khan, S. H. and M. A. Basir. 1965.
Scutellonema mangiferae n. sp. (Nematoda: Hoplolaimidae) from India. :: Proc. Helminth. Soc. Washington 32(2): 136-138.

979. Khera, S. 1965.
Nematodes from the banks of still and running waters. I. Tridontus longicaudatus n. g., n. sp., subfamily Diplogasterinae Micoletzky, 1922 from India. :: Nematologica 11(2): 249-254.

980. Killick, J. L. 1964.
A new species of the genus Anaplectus de Coninck and Schuurmans Stekhoven, 1933 (Nematoda, Plectidae). :: New Zealand J. Sci. 7(2): 165-168.

981. Kirjanova, E. S. 1938.
Materials on the nematode fauna of Scorzonera Tau-saghyz Lipsch. and Bossé [Russian Text]. [In The pests and diseases of rubber-bearing plants.] :: All-Union Rubber and Guttapercha Scient. Res. Inst., ONTI, Moscow 1938, Series 2: 76-86.

982. Kirjanova, E. S. 1961.
Some nematological problems of plants, soils, and insects [Russian Text]. :: Publ. Univ. Samarkand, Uzbekstan SSR, 1-161.

983. Kirjanova, E. S. 1962.
Heterodera oxiana, sp. nov. (Nematodes: Heteroderidae) from Kara-Kalpakia [Russian Text]. [In Harmful nematodes of agricultural plants and their control.] :: Proc. Fifth All-Union Symposium of Phytonematologists. Publ. Univ. Samarkand, Uzbekstan SSR: 122-131.

984. Kirjanova, E. S. 1963.
Collection and taxonomy of root nematodes of the family Heteroderidae (Skarbilovich, 1947) Thorne, 1949 [Russian Text]. :: pp. 6-32. Methods of Investigating Nematodes in Plants, Soils and Insects. Acad. Sci. USSR, Moscow, 174 pp.

984a. Kirjanova, E. S. and T. S. Ivanova. [1965].
On the nematode fauna of Pelargonium roseum L. in Tadzhikistan [Russian Text]. :: Izvest. Otdel. Biol. Nauk, Akad. Nauk Tadzhik. SSR 1(18): 24-31.

985. Kirjanova, E. S. and E. Krall. 1963.
The Estonian cyst-forming nematode— Heterodera estonica n. sp. (Nematodes; Heteroderidae) [Estonian Text]. :: Eesti NSV Teaduste Akad. Toimet., Biol. Seer. 12(3): 219-223.

985a. Kirjanova, E. S. and E. Krall. 1965.
The milfoil cyst nematode—Heterodera millefolii n. sp. (Nematodes: Heteroderidae) [Russian Text]. :: Eesti NSV Teaduste Akad. Toimet., Biol. Seer., 14(3): 325-328.

986. Konicek, D. E. and H. J. Jensen. 1961.
Longidorus menthasolanus, a new plant parasite from Oregon (Nemata: Dorylaimoidea). :: Proc. Helminth. Soc. Washington 28(2): 216-218.

987. Kozlowska, J. and L. Roguska-Wasilewska. 1963.
A new species of the genus Cephalobus Bast. 1865 (Cephalobus mucronatus n. sp.) and observations on its occurrence. :: Bull. Acad. Polon. Sci., Cl. II, 11(5): 247-249.

988. Krall, E. 1963.
Criconema kirjanovae n. sp.—A new plant parasitic nematode from the Estonian S.S.R. [Russian Text]. :: Eesti NSV Teaduste Akad. Toimet., Biol. Seer., 12(4): 342-344.

989. Kruger, S. P. 1965.
New species of the genera Tylencholaimus and Dorylaimellus from South Africa. :: Proc. Helminth. Soc. Washington 32(1): 1-7.

990. Kuiper, K. and P. A. A. Loof. 1962.
Trichodorus flevensis n. sp. (Nematoda: Enoplida). A plant nematode from new polder soil. :: Versl. Meded. Plantenz. Dienst 136(1961): 193-200.

990a. Lazarevskaja, S. L. [1961].
On the helminthofauna of *Acanthocinus aedilis* (Cerambiciidae) [Russian Text]. :: Helminthologia, Bratislava 3: 212-220.

990b. Lazarevskaja, S. L. [1964].
Acrostichus minimus n. sp. (Diplogasteroididae)—new nematode from Acanthocinus aedilis [Russian Text]. :: Proc. Helm. Lab. Acad. Sci. USSR 14: 122-127.

990c. Lazarevskaja, S. L. [1965].
Filipjevella gen. n. (Nematoda, Diplogasteroididae). :: Proc. Helm. Lab. Acad. Sci. USSR 16: 61-67.

991. Lee, D. L. 1961.
Two new species of cryptobiotic (anabiotic) freshwater nematodes, *Actinolaimus hintoni* and *Dorylaimus keilini* sp. nov. (Dorylaimidae). :: Parasitology 51: 237-240.

992. Lima, M. B. and M. R. Siddiqi. 1963.
Boleodorus volutus n. sp. (Nematoda: Nothotylenchinae) found in soil about grass roots in England. :: Nematologica 9(1): 19-23.

993. Loof, P. A. A. 1960.
Taxonomic studies on the genus *Pratylenchus* (Nematoda). :: Tijdschr. Plantenziekten. 66: 29-90.

994. Loof, P. A. A. 1961.
On the identity of *Dorylaimus robustus* de Man. :: Nematologica 6(1): 42-48.

995. Loof, P. A. A. 1961.
The nematode collection of Dr. J. G. de Man. :: Meded. Lab. Fytopath. 190: 169-254.

996. Loof, P. A. A. 1961.
Tylenchus gulosus Kühn, 1890: proposed suppression under the plenary powers (Nematoda). Z. N. (S) 1432. :: Bull. Zool. Nomencl. 18(3): 206-207.

997. Loof, P. A. A. 1962.
Metacrobeles togoensis n. gen., n. sp., a remarkable acrobelin nematode from a diseased coconut tree. :: Nematologica 7(2): 114-118.

998. Loos, P. A. A. 1963.
A new species of *Telotylenchus* (Nematoda: Tylenchida). :: Nematologica 9(1): 76-80.

999. Loof, P. A. A. 1964.
A review of the nematode genus *Leptonchus* (Enoplida). :: Nematologica 9(4) (1963): 507-520.

1000. Loof, P. A. A. 1964.
Four new species of *Criconemoides* from the Netherlands. :: Versl. Pl. Ziek. Dienst 141: 160-168.

1001. Loof, P. A. A. 1964.
Free-living and plant-parasitic nematodes from Venezuela. :: Nematologica 10(2): 201-300.

1001a. Loof, P. A. A. 1965.
Zur Taxonomie von Criconemoides rusticus (Micoletzky) und C. informis (Micoletzky). :: Mitt. Zool. Mus. Berlin 41(2): 183-192.

1001b. Loof, P. A. A. 1965.
Trichodorus anemones n. sp. with a note on *T. teres* Hooper, 1962 (Nematoda: Enoplida). :: Versl. Pl. Ziek. 142: 132-136.

1002. Loof, P. A. A. and M. S. Jairajpuri. 1965.
Two new species of *Chronogaster* Cobb, 1913 (Nematoda: Plectidae). :: Proc. Helminth. Soc. Washington 32(2): 181-186.

1003. Loof, P. A. A. and M. Oostenbrink. 1962.
Rotylenchulus borealis n. sp. with a key to the species of *Rotylenchulus*. :: Nematologica 7(1): 83-90.

References 1004 – 1018

1004. Lordello, L. G. E. 1963.
Nôvo gênero de nematóide do solo, da família *Actinolaimidae*. :: An. Acad. Brasil. Cien. 35(4): 591-592.

1004a. Lordello, L. G. E. 1965.
Contribution to the knowledge of the Brazilian nematodes of the family *Dorylaimidae* [Portuguese Text]. :: Thesis no. 9 (Zool., Anat. Fisiol. Compar. Anim. Domés.) Esc. Sup. Agr. "Luiz de Queiroz," Univ. São Paulo, Piracicaba, Brazil: 1-68, pls. 1-2.

1004b. Lordello, L. G. E. and C. P. da Costa. 1961.
A new nematode parasite of coffee roots in Brazil. :: Rev. Brasil. Biol. 21(4): 363-366.

1005. Lordello, L. G. E. and A. J. de Oliveira. 1963.
Nematódeos associados a uma doença da palmeira imperial. :: Rev. Brasil. Biol. 23(1): 19-24.

1006. Lordello, L. G. E. and A. P. L. Zamith. 1960.
"Meloidogyne coffeicola" sp. n., a pest of coffee trees in the state of Paraná, Brazil (Nematoda, Heteroderidae). :: Rev. Brasil. Biol. 20(4): 375-379.

1007. Lordello, L. G. E., A. P. L. Zamith, and O. J. Boock. 1961.
Two nematodes found attacking potato in Cochabamba, Bolivia. :: An. Acad. Brasil. Cien. 33(2): 209-215.

1008. Luc, M. 1960.
Dolichodorus profundus n. sp. (Nematoda-Tylenchida). :: Nematologica 5(1): 1-6.

1009. Luc, M. 1960.
Three new species of the genus *Rotylenchoides* Whitehead, 1958 (Nematoda-Tylenchida) [French Text]. :: Nematologica 5(1): 7-17.

1010. Luc, M. 1961.
Xiphinema de l'Ouest Africain (Nematoda-Dorylaimoidea) Deuxième Note. :: Nematologica 6(2): 107-122.

1011. Luc, M. and R. B. Berdon Brizuela. 1961.
Heterodera oryzae n. sp. (Nematoda-Tylenchoidea) parasite du riz en Côte d'Ivoire. :: Nematologica 6(4): 272-279.

1012. Luc, M. and F. E. Caveness. 1963.
Dolichodorus nigeriensis n. sp. (Nematoda: Dolichodoridae). :: Proc. Helminth. Soc. Washington 30(2): 297-299.

1013. Luc, M. and A. Dalmasso. 1964.
Three new species of *Xiphinema* associated with vine [French Text]. :: Nematologica 9(4) (1963): 531-541.

1014. Luc, M. and J. B. Goodey. 1962.
Hirschmannia n. g. differentiated from *Radopholus* Thorne, 1949 (Nematoda: Tylenchoidea). :: Nematologica 7(3): 197-202.

1015. Luc, M. and J. B. Goodey. 1964.
Hirschmanniella nom. nov. for *Hirschmannia*. :: Nematologica 9(3) (1963): 471.

1015a. Luc, M. and G. de Guiran. 1960.
Les nématodes associés aux plantes de l'Ouest Africain, liste préliminaire. :: Agron. Trop. (Paris) 15(4): 434-449.

1016. Luc, M. and G. de Guiran. 1962.
Deux nouveaux *Paratylenchus* (Nematoda-Criconematidae) de Côte d'Ivoire. :: Nematologica 7(2): 133-138.

1017. Luc, M., M. B. Lima, B. Weischer and J. J. M. Flegg. 1964.
Xiphinema vuittenezi n. sp. (Nematoda: Dorylaimidae). :: Nematologica 10(1): 151-163.

1018. Luc, M. and G. Merny. 1963.
Heterodera sacchari n. sp. (Nematoda: Tylenchoidea) parasite de la canne à sucre au Congo-Brazzaville. :: Nematologica: 9(1): 31-37.

1019. Luc, M. and A. C. Tarjan. 1963.
Note systématique sur le genre *Xiphinema* Cobb, 1913 (Nematoda: Dorylaimidae). :: Nematologica 9(1): 111-115.

1020. Maggenti, A. R. 1961.
Revision of the genus *Plectus* (Nematoda: Plectidae). :: Proc. Helminth. Soc. Washington 28(2): 139-166.

1021. Maggenti, A. R. 1962.
The production of the gelatinous matrix and its taxonomic significance in *Tylenchulus* (Nematoda: Tylenchulinae). :: Proc. Helminth. Soc. Washington 29(2): 139-144.

1022. Marinari, Anna. 1962.
Tylenchorhynchus goodeyi n. sp. (*Tylenchinae: Nematoda*). :: Redia 47: 119-122.

1023. Massey, C. L. 1956.
Nematode parasites and associates of the Engelmann spruce beetle (*Dendroctonus engelmanni* Hopk.). :: Proc. Helminth. Soc. Washington 23(1): 14-24.

1024. Massey, C. L. 1962.
New species of Diplogasteridae (Nematoda) associated with bark beetles in the United States. :: Proc. Helminth. Soc. Washington 29(1): 67-75.

1025. Massey, C. L. 1963.
Santafea new genus (Rhabditoidea, Chambersiellidae) and a change in the systematic position of *Macrolaimus* Maupas 1900. :: Proc. Helminth. Soc. Washington 30(1): 26-28.

1025a. Massey, C. L. 1964.
The nematode parasites and associates of the fir engraver beetle, *Scolytus ventralis* Le Conte, in New Mexico. :: J. Insect. Path. 6: 133-155.

1026. Meagher, J. W. 1964.
Tylodorus acuminatus n. g., n. sp. (Nematoda: Tylenchinae) from *Eucalyptus* forest in Australia. :: Nematologica 9(4) (1963): 635-640.

1027. Merny, G. 1964.
Un nouveau Tylenchida d'Afrique tropicale: *Tetylenchus annulatus* n. sp. :: Nematologica 10(3): 425-430.

1027a. Meyl, A. H. 1957.
Über einige Süsswasser-Nematoden aus Peru insbesondere aus dem Nicaragua-See. :: Arch. Hydrobiol. 53(4): 520-526.

1028. Meyl, A. H. 1961.
Die freilebenden Erd- und Süsswasser-nematoden (Fadenwürmer). :: *In* Die Tierwelt Mitteleuropas. Quelle and Meyer, Leipzig, 164 pp., 54 tab.

1029. Milne, D. L. [1963].
A revision of the genus *Prismatolaimus* de Man, 1880, with a key to the species and a description of *P. parvus* n. sp. :: South African J. Agr. Sci. 6(3): 549-555.

1030. Mulvey, R. H. 1961.
The Mononchidae: A family of predaceous nematodes. I. Genus Mylonchulus (Enoplida: Mononchidae). :: Canad. J. Zool. 39(5): 665-696.

1031. Mulvey, R. H. 1961.
The Mononchidae: a family of predaceous nematodes. II. Genus Anatonchus (Enoplida: Mononchidae). :: Canad. J. Zool. 39: 807-826.

1032. Mulvey, R. H. 1962.
The Mononchidae: a family of predaceous nematodes. III. Genus Miconchus (Enoplida: Mononchidae). :: Canad. J. Zool. 40: 65-81.

1033. Mulvey, R. H. 1963.
The Mononchidae: a family of predaceous nematodes. IV. Genus Iotonchus (Enoplida: Mononchidae). :: Canad. J. Zool. 41: 79-98.

1034. Mulvey, R. H. 1963.
The Mononchidae: a family of predaceous nematodes. V. Genera Sporonchulus, Granonchulus, and Prionchuloides n. gen. (Enoplida: Mononchidae). :: Canad. J. Zool. 41: 763-774.

1035. Nakasono, K. and M. Ichinohe. 1961.
Hemicriconemoides kanayaensis n. sp. associated with tea root in Japan (Nematoda: Criconematidae). :: Japan. J. Appl. Zool. 5(4): 273-276.

1036. Nickle, W. R. 1963.
Bovienema (Nematoda: Allantonematidae), a new genus parasitizing bark beetles of the genus *Pityogenes* Bedel, with notes on other endoparasitic nematodes of scolytids. :: Proc. Helminth. Soc. Washington 30(2): 256-262.

1037. Norton, D. C. 1965.
Anguina agropyronifloris n. sp., infecting florets of *Agropyron smithii*. :: Proc. Helminth. Soc. Washington 32(2): 118-122.

1038. Oostenbrink, M. 1960.
The family Criconematidae, chapt. 17, pp. 196-205. :: *In* J. N. Sasser and W. R. Jenkins, (eds.), Nematology fundamentals and recent advances with emphasis on plant parasites and soil forms. Univ. North Carolina Press, Chapel Hill.

1039. Orr, C. C. and O. J. Dickerson. 1965.
Tylencholaimellus cinctus n. sp. (Dorylaimoidea: Leptonchidae) from Kansas. :: Proc. Helminth. Soc. Washington 32(2): 191-193.

1040. Paramonov, A. A. 1964.
Fundamentals of Phytonematology II [Russian Text]. :: Acad. of Sci., U.S.S.R., Moscow, 444 pp.

1040a. Penso, G. 1939.
Su due Anguilluline parassite dei banani della Somalia Italiana. :: Rend. Inst. San. Pub., Roma 2(3): 849-852.

1040b. Penso, G. 1941.
Su di una Anguillulina parassita delle patate. :: Rend. Inst. San. Pub., Roma 4(3): 585-590, figs. 1-18.

1041. Poghossian, Hermine E. 1960.
New species of nematode—Meloidodera armeniaca n. sp. (Nematoda: Heteroderidae) from the Armenian SSR [Russian Text]. :: Rept. Acad. Sci. Armenian SSR 31(5): 311-313.

1042. Poghossian, Hermine E. 1961.
A new species of nematode Heterodera rumicis sp. n. from the Armenian SSR [Russian Text]. :: Rept. Acad. Sci. Armenian SSR 32(3): 171-175.

1043. Poinar, G. O. 1965.
An association between *Pelodera* (*Coarctadera*) *acarambates* n. sp. (Rhabditina: Nematoda) and Macrochelid mites (Mesostigmata: Acari). :: Nematologica 10(4) (1964): 507-511.

1043a. Pokrovskaya, T. V. [1964].
Micronema intermedia sp. nova (Nematoda, Panagrolaimidae). :: Helminthologia, Bratislava 5: 73-75.

1043b. Prasad, S. K., E. Khan and V. K. Mathur. [1965].
Criconemoides georgii n. sp. (Nematoda: Criconematidae) from India. :: Current Sci., Bangalore 34(23): 667-668.

1043c. Railliet, A. [1896].
Quelques rectifications à la nomenclature des parasites. :: Rec. Méd. Vét. 73(8): 157-161.

1043d. Ramírez, Carmen T. 1964.
Hoplolaimus puertoricensis n. sp. (Nematoda: Hoplolaimidae). :: J. Agr. Univ. Puerto Rico 48(2): 127-130.

1044. Raski, D. J. 1962.
Paratylenchidae n. fam. with descriptions of five new species of *Gracilacus* n. g. and an emendation of *Cacopaurus* Thorne, 1943, *Paratylenchus* Micoletzky, 1922 and Criconematidae Thorne, 1943. :: Proc. Helminth. Soc. Washington 29(2): 189-207.

1045. Raski, D. J., S. K. Prasad and G. Swarup. 1964.
Telotylenchus housei a new nematode species from Mysore State, India (Tylenchidae: Nematoda). :: Nematologica 10(1): 83-86.

1046. Rau, G. J. 1963.
Three new species of *Belonolaimus* (Nematoda: Tylenchida) with additional data on *B. longicaudatus* and *B. gracilis.* :: Proc. Helminth. Soc. Washington 30(1): 119-128.

1047. Rau, G. J. and G. Fassuliotis. 1965.
Hypsoperine spartinae n. sp., a gall-forming nematode on the roots of smooth cordgrass. :: Proc. Helminth. Soc. Washington 32(2): 159-162.

1048. Reed, J. P. and W. R. Jenkins. 1963.
Hemicycliophora vaccinium n. sp. (*Nematoda: Criconematidae*) from cranberry. :: Proc. Helminth. Soc. Washington 30(2): 211-212.

1049. Riffle, J. W. 1963.
Meloidogyne ovalis (Nematoda: Heteroderidae), a new species of root-knot nematode. :: Proc. Helminth. Soc. Washington 30(2): 287-292.

1050. Román, J. 1961.
A new species of the genus *Helicotylenchus* (Nematoda: Hoplolaimidae) attacking sugarcane. :: J. Agr. Univ. Puerto Rico 45(4): 300-303.

1051. Román, J. 1962.
Trophurus longimarginatus n. sp. (Tylenchida: Nematoda) from Puerto Rico. :: J. Agr. Univ. Puerto Rico 46(4): 269-271.

1051a. Román, J. 1964.
Belonolaimus lineatus n. sp. (*Nematoda: Tylenchida*). :: J. Agr. Univ. Puerto Rico 48(2): 131-134.

1052. Román, J. 1965.
Nematodes of Puerto Rico, the genus Helicotylenchus Steiner, 1945 (Nematoda: Hoplolaiminae). :: Univ. Puerto Rico Agr. Exp. Sta. Tech. Paper 41, 23 pp.

1053. Romaniko, V. I. 1960.
New studies on the biology and ecology of Pratylenchus globulicola Romaniko, nov. sp. (Nematodes, Pratylenchidae) attacking beans (Leguminosae) [Russian Text]. :: *In* Material from the All-Union Conference on the Study of Nematodes, Oct. 3-8, 1960, Samarkand, 85-87.

1054. Rühm, W. 1960.
Ein Beitrag zur Nomenklatur und Systematik einiger mit Scolytiden vergesellschafteter Nematodenarten. :: Zool. Anz., Leipzig 164(5-6): 201-213.

1055. Rühm, W. 1962.
Zur Variabilität der Cuticularstruktur der Unterfamilie Bunonematinae Sachs 1949 sowie eine Neubeschreibung von *Bunonema* (*Rhodolaimus*) *voulliemei* n. sp. :: Nematologica 7(1): 37-52.

1055a. Rühm, W. 1964.
Ein Beitrag zur Vergesellschaftung zwischen Nematoden und Insekten (*Pelodera bakeri* n. sp. [*Nematoda, Rhabditoidea, Rhabditidae*] eine mit *Calvertius tuberosus* Perm. *et.* Germ. [*Coleoptera, Curculionidae, Hylobiinae*] vergesellschaftete Nematodenart an *Araucaria araucana* [Mol.] Koch). :: Zool. Anz., Leipzig 173 (3): 212-220.

1055b. Rühm, W. 1965.
Zur "Wirtskreiserweiterung" einer mit Borkenkäfern (Scolytoidea, Col.) vergesellschafteten Nematodenart. :: Ztschr. Parasitenk. 26: 230-253.

1055c. Rühm, W. 1965.
Brutbiologie und Morphologie einer Scolytidenart als Voraussetzung einer neuartigen Spezialisierung zweier Nematodenarten. :: Ztschr. Ang. Entomol. 55(3): 264-275.

1056. Rühm, W. and C. Chararas. [1957].
Description, biologie et histologie de quatre espèces nouvelles de nematodes parasites de *Dryocoetes hectographus* Reit. (Col. Scolytidae). :: Entomophaga 2(4): 253-269.

1057. Sanwal, K. C. 1960. Macrolaimus canadensis n. sp. (Nematoda: Panagrolaiminae), from the frass of the bark beetle Phloeosinus canadensis Swaine, 1917, with remarks on other species of the genus Macrolaimus Maupas, 1900. :: Canad. J. Zool. 38(6): 1127-1131.

1058. Sanwal, K. C. 1960. Panagrellus dubius n. sp. (Nematoda: Turbatricinae Goodey, 1943) from frass of beetle Sternochetus lapathi (L.), with remarks on redescriptions of Anguillula rediviva (L., 1767). :: Canad. J. Zool. 38(6): 1041-1046.

1059. Sanwal, K. C. 1960. Taxonomic position of Macrolaimus papillatus (Rahm, 1928) Goodey, 1951, status of Diastolaimus Rahm, 1928, and emended diagnosis of Chambersiellidae and Chambersiella Cobb, 1920 (Nematoda). :: Canad. J. Zool. 38: 751-753.

1060. Sanwal, K. C. 1961. A key to the species of the nematode genus Aphelenchoides Fischer, 1894. :: Canad. J. Zool. 39: 143-148.

1061. Sanwal, K. C. 1961. Aphelenchoides subparietinus n. sp. (Nematoda: Aphelenchoididae) from diseased lily bulbs. :: Canad. J. Zool. 39(5): 573-577.

1061a. Sanwal, K. C. 1965. Two new species of the genus Aphelenchoides Fischer, 1894 (Nematoda: Aphelenchoididae) from the Canadian Arctic. :: Canad. J. Zool. 43: 933-940.

1061b. Schiemer, F. [1965]. Diagnose von *Enchodelus microdorus* n. sp. (Nematodes, Dorylaimidae). :: Zool. Anz., Leipzig 175 (4/6): 413-415.

1062. Schoemaker, R. L. P. Wolff. 1963. *Gracilacus peperpotti* n. sp. (Nematoda: Paratylenchidae) found in a Surinam coffee plantation soil. :: Nematologica 9(2): 296-299.

1062a. Schuurmans Stekhoven, J. H. 1954. Neorhabditis, a new name for Parahabditis [*sic*] Schuurmans Stekhoven. :: Proc. Helminth. Soc. Washington 21(1): 47.

1063. Seinhorst, J. W. 1963. A redescription of the male of the *Trichodorus primitivus* (de Man), and the description of a new species *T. similis*. :: Nematologica 9(1): 125-130.

1064. Seinhorst, J. W. 1963. Five new *Tylenchorhynchus* species from West Africa. :: Nematologica 9(2): 173-180.

1065. Sher, S. A. 1961. Revision of the Hoplolaiminae (Nematoda). I. Classification of nominal genera and nominal species. :: Nematologica 6(2): 155-169.

1066. Sher, S. A. 1963. Revision of the Hoplolaiminae (Nematoda). II. *Hoplolaimus* Daday, 1905 and *Aorolaimus* n. gen. :: Nematologica 9(2): 267-295.

1067. Sher, S. A. 1964. Revision of the Hoplolaiminae (Nematoda). III. *Scutellonema* Andrássy, 1958. :: Nematologica 9(3) (1963): 421-443.

1068. Sher, S. A. 1964. Revision of the Hoplolaiminae (Nematoda). IV. *Peltamigratus* n. gen. :: Nematologica 9(3) (1963): 455-467.

1069. Sher, S. A. 1965. *Aphasmatylenchus nigeriensis* n. gen., n. sp. (Aphasmatylenchinae n. subfam.: Tylenchoidea: Nematoda) from Nigerian soil. :: Proc. Helminth. Soc. Washington 32(2): 172-176.

1070. Sher, S. A. 1965. *Aphelenchus steueri* Stefański, 1916 (Nematoda): proposed suppression under the plenary powers. Z.N. (S.) 1698. :: Bull. Zool. Nomencl. 22(3): 195.

References 1071 – 1087

1071. Sher, S. A. 1965.
Revision of the Hoplolaiminae (Nematoda). V. *Rotylenchus* Filipjev, 1936. ::
Nematologica 11(2): 173-198.

1072. Shinohara, T. 1960.
Studies on *Rhabditis* (Nematoda, Rhabditidae). I. *Rhabditis* spp. obtained from human feces. II. On *Rhabditis* spp. found in the alimentary organs of mollusca, *Fruticicola* (*Acusta*) *sieboldiana* (Pfeiffer) and *Limax* (*Limacus*) *flavus* Linné [Japanese Text]. :: J. Kurume Med. Assn. 23(7): 2777-2819.

1073. Siddiqi, M. R. 1960.
Telotylenchus, a new nematode genus from North India (Tylenchida: Telotylenchinae n. sub-fam). :: Nematologica 5(2): 73-77.

1074. Siddiqi, M. R. 1961.
A new species of the genus *Paurodontus* Thorne, 1941 (Nematoda: Neotylenchidae) from India. :: Proc. Helminth. Soc. Washington 28(2): 213-215.

1075. Siddiqi, M. R. 1961.
Gymnotylenchus zeae, n.g., n. sp. (Nematoda: Neotylenchidae), a root associate of *Zea mays* L. (sweet corn) in Aligarh, North India. :: Nematologica 6(1): 59-63.

1076. Siddiqi, M. R. 1961.
On *Xiphinema opisthohysterum*, n. sp., and *X. pratense* Loos, 1949, two dorylaimid nematodes attacking fruit trees in India. :: Ztschr. Parasitenk. 20: 457-465.

1077. Siddiqi, M. R. 1961.
Studies on species of Criconematinae (Nematoda: Tylenchida) from India. :: Proc. Helminth. Soc. Washington 28(1): 19-34.

1078. Siddiqi, M. R. 1961.
Studies on *Tylenchorhynchus* spp. (Nematoda: Tylenchida) from India. :: Ztschr. Parasitenk. 21: 46-64.

1079. Siddiqi, M. R. 1962.
Longidorus tarjani n. sp. found around oak roots in Florida. :: Nematologica 8(2): 152-156.

1080. Siddiqi, M. R. 1962.
Studies on the genus *Longidorus* Micoletzky, 1922 (Nematoda: Dorylaimoidea), with descriptions of three new species. :: Proc. Helminth. Soc. Washington 29(2): 177-188.

1081. Siddiqi, M. R. 1962.
Trichodorus pakistanensis n. sp. (Nematoda: Trichodoridae) with observations on *T. porosus* Allen, 1957, *T. mirzai* Siddiqi, 1960, and *T. minor* Colbran, 1956, from India. :: Nematologica 8(3): 193-200.

1082. Siddiqi, M. R. 1963.
Four new species in the sub-family Tylenchinae (Nematoda) from North India. :: Ztschr. Parasitenk. 23: 397-404.

1083. Siddiqi, M. R. 1963.
Four new species of the genus *Tylenchus* Bastian, 1865 (Nematoda) from North India. :: Ztschr. Parasitenk. 23: 170-180.

1084. Siddiqi, M. R. 1963.
On the classification of the Pratylenchidae (Thorne, 1949) nov. grad. (Nematoda: Tylenchida) with a description of *Zygotylenchus browni* nov. gen. et nov. sp. :: Ztschr. Parasitenk. 23: 390-396.

1085. Siddiqi, M. R. 1963.
On the diagnosis of the nematode genera *Psilenchus* de Man, 1921, and *Basiria* Siddiqi, 1959, with a description of *Psilenchus hilarus* n. sp. :: Ztschr. Parasitenk. 23: 164-169.

1086. Siddiqi, M. R. 1963.
On the identity of *Belonolaimus hastulatus* Colbran, 1960, and *Tylenchorhynchus indicus* Siddiqi, 1961 (Nematoda: Tylenchida). :: Current Sci. Bangalore, 32(12): 550-551.

1087. Siddiqi, M. R. 1963.
Trichodorus spp. (Nematoda: Trichodoridae) from Tunisia and Nicaragua. :: Nematologica 9(1): 69-75.

References 1088 – 1099

1088. Siddiqi, M. R. 1963.
Two new species of the genus *Helicotylenchus* Steiner, 1945 (Nematoda: Hoplolaiminae). :: Ztschr. Parasitenk. 23: 239-244.

1089. Siddiqi, M. R. 1964.
Four new species in the family Belondiridae (Nematoda: Dorylaimida). :: Labdev J. Sci. Tech. 2(1): 37-41.

1090. Siddiqi, M. R. 1964.
Helicotylenchus mucronatus n. sp. and *H. tunisiensis* n. sp. (Nematoda: Hoplolaiminae). :: Nematologica 9(3) (1963): 386-390.

1090a. Siddiqi, M. R. 1964.
On the occurrence of Enchodorella okhlaensis Jairajpuri & Siddiqi, 1964 in Jhelum City, West Pakistan, with notes on the synonymy of Nordia Jairajpuri & Siddiqi, 1964 (Nematoda: Dorylaimida). :: Labdev J. Sci. Tech. 2(3): 208.

1091. Siddiqi, M. R. 1964.
Radopholus williamsi n. sp. (Nematoda: Pratylenchidae), a parasite of sugarcane roots at L'Etoile, Mauritius. :: Indian J. Ent. 26(2): 207-208.

1092. Siddiqi, M. R. 1964.
Rotylenchus eximius n. sp. (Nematoda: Hoplolaiminae) found around almond roots in Tunisia. :: Nematologica 10(1): 101-104.

1092a. Siddiqi, M. R. 1964.
Six new nematode species in the superfamily Dorylaimoidea from India. :: Labdev J. Sci. Tech. 2(2): 136-144.

1093. Siddiqi, M. R. 1964.
Three new species of *Dorylaimoides* Thorne & Swanger, 1936, with a description of *Xiphinema orbum* n. sp. (Nematoda: Dorylaimoidea). :: Nematologica 9(4) (1963): 626-634.

1093a. Siddiqi, M. R. 1964.
Tylencholaimus macrurus n. sp. (Nematoda: Dorylaimidae) from jungle soil in Karwi (U.P.), India. :: Labdev J. Sci. Tech. 2(4): 266.

1094. Siddiqi, M. R. 1964.
Xiphinema conurum n. sp. and *Paralongidorus microlaimus* n. sp., with a key to the species of *Paralongidorus* (Nematoda: Longidoridae). :: Proc. Helminth. Soc. Washington 31(2): 133-137.

1095. Siddiqi, M. R. 1965.
Criconemoides citricola n. sp. (Nematoda: Criconematidae), with a redescription of *Criconema murrayi* (Southern, 1914). :: Nematologica 11(2): 239-243.

1096. Siddiqi, M. R. 1965.
Five new species of soil nematodes in the genera *Dorylaimoides* Thorne & Swanger, 1936, and *Discolaimium* Thorne, 1939, from India. :: Nematologica 11(1): 100-108.

1097. Siddiqi, M. R. 1965.
Longidorus nirulai n. sp., a parasite of potato plants in Shillong, India, with a key to species of *Longidorus* (Nematoda: Dorylaimoidea). :: Proc. Helminth. Soc. Washington 32(1): 95-99.

1098. Siddiqi, M. R. 1965.
Seven new species of Dorylaimoidea (Nematoda) from India, with descriptions of *Lenonchium* n. gen. and *Galophinema* n. gen. :: Proc. Helminth. Soc. Washington 32(1): 81-90.

1098a. Siddiqi, M. R. 1965.
Studies on the genus *Thornenema* Andrássy, 1959, (Nematoda Dorylaimidae), with descriptions of two new species and *T. cavalcantii* (Lordello, 1955) from India. :: Labdev J. Sci. Tech. 3(2): 128-133.

1099. Siddiqi, M. R. and M. A. Basir. 1959.
On some plant-parasitic nematodes occurring in South India, with the description of two new species of the genus *Tylenchorhynchus* Cobb, 1913. :: Proc. 46th Meet. Indian Sci. Cong., Pt. IV (Abs.): 35.

1100. Siddiqi, M. R. and M. A. Basir. 1965.
Amphidelus sylvaticus n. sp. and *A. candidus* n. sp. (Nematoda: Alaimina) from India, with a key to the species of *Amphidelus*. :: Nematologica 11(3): 343-348.

1101. Siddiqi, M. R. and K. F. Brown. 1964.
Helicoytlenchus [sic] *retusus* n. sp. (Nematoda: Hoplolaiminae) found around sugar cane roots in Negros Oriental, Philippines. :: Proc. Helminth. Soc. Washington 31(2): 209-211.

1102. Siddiqi, M. R. and K. F. Brown. 1965.
Trichodorus rhodesiensis and *Amphidelus trichurus,* two new nematode species from cultivated soils of Africa. :: Proc. Helminth. Soc. Washington 32(2): 239-242.

1103. Siddiqi, M. R. and J. B. Goodey. 1964.
The status of the genera and subfamilies of the Criconematidae (Nematoda); with a comment on the position of *Fergusobia*. :: Nematologica 9(3) (1963): 363-377.

1104. Siddiqi, M. R., D. J. Hooper and E. Khan. 1963.
A new nematode genus *Paralongidorus* (Nematoda: Dorylaimoidea) with descriptions of two new species and observations on *Paralongidorus citri* (Siddiqi 1959) n. comb. :: Nematologica: 9(1): 7-14.

1105. Siddiqi, M. R. and Z. Husain. 1964.
Three new species of nematodes in the family Hoplolaimidae found attacking citrus trees in India. :: Proc. Helminth. Soc. Washington 31(2): 211-215.

1106. Siddiqi, M. R. and Z. Husain. 1965.
Paralongidorus beryllus n. sp. (Nematoda: Dorylaimoidea) from India. :: Proc. Helminth. Soc. Washington 32(2): 243-245.

1107. Siddiqi, M. R. and E. Khan. 1964.
Tylencholaimellus eskei n. sp. (Nematoda: Leptonchidae), with a key to the species of *Tylencholaimellus*. :: Nematologica 10(1): 105-107.

1108. Siddiqi, M. R. and E. Khan. 1964.
Xenonchium cedari n. g., n. sp. and Proleptonchus indicus n. sp. (Nematoda: Dorylaimoidea) from North India. :: Labdev J. Sci. Tech. 2(1): 34-36.

1109. Siddiqi, M. R. and E. Khan. 1965.
A review of the nematode genus *Basirotyleptus* (Dorylaimida) with descriptions of two new species. :: Proc. Helminth. Soc. Washington 32(1): 23-31.

1110. Siddiqi, M. R. and S. H. Khan. 1964.
Trichonchium n. g. (Nematoda: Campydoridae), with descriptions of two new species from tea soil, Assam, India. :: Nematologica 9(4) (1963): 641-645.

1111. Siddiqi, M. R. and J. F. Southey. 1962.
Criconema palmatum n. sp. (Nematoda: Criconematidae) from North Devon, England. :: Nematologica 8 (3): 221-224.

1112. Skarbilovich, T. S. [1957].
Contribution to knowledge of nematodes of clover [Russian Text]. :: Summaries of Communications, Sci. Conf. All-Union Soc. Helminth. 2: 68-69.

1113. Skarbilovich, T. S. [1958].
Parasitic nematodes of clover and maize on collective farms of the Moscow, Voronezh, Lipetsk and Smolensk regions [Russian Text]. :: Proc. All-Union Inst. Helminth. 4: 71-74.

1114. Skarbilovich, T. S. and L. F. Potekhina. [1959].
Observations on nematodes in *Panax ginseng* [Russian Text]. :: Proc. All-Union Inst. Helminth. 6: 411-414.

1115. Sledge, E. B. and J. R. Christie. 1962.
Sphaeronema whittoni n. sp. (Nematoda: Criconematidae). :: Nematologica 8(1): 11-14.

1116. Sledge, E. B. and A. M. Golden. 1964.
Hypsoperine graminis (Nematoda: Heteroderidae), a new genus and species of plant-parasitic nematode. :: Proc. Helminth. Soc. Washington 31(1): 83-88.

1116a. Stanković, S. [1932].
Die Fauna des Ohridsees und ihre Herkunft. :: Arch. Hydrobiol. 23(4): 557-617, pls. 26-27.

1117. Stoianov, D. 1964.
A contribution to the nematode fauna of the grape vine [Bulgarian Text]. :: Plant Protection (Bulgarian Ministry Agr.) 6: 16-24.

1118. Sturhan, D. 1963.
Beitrag zur Systematik der Gattung Longidorus. :: Nematologica 9(1): 131-142.

1119. Sturhan, D. 1963.
Beitrag zur Systematik der Gattung Xiphinema Cobb 1913. :: Nematologica 9(2): 205-214.

1120. Sturhan, D. and W. Friedman. 1965.
Ditylenchus convallariae n. sp. (Nematoda: Tylenchida). :: Nematologica 11(2): 219-223.

1121. Sturhan, D. and B. Weischer. 1964.
Longidorus vineacola n. sp. (Nematoda: Dorylaimidae). :: Nematologica 10(2): 335-341.

1121a. Sumenkova, N. I. [1964].
New species Cervidellus devimucronatus nov. sp. (Nematoda; Cephalobidae) [Russian Text]. :: Proc. Helm. Lab. Acad. Sci. USSR 14: 234-237.

1121b. Sumenkova, N. I. [1965].
A new species Panagrolaimus longicaudatus n. sp. (Nematoda, Panagrolaimidae) from cultivated mushroom [Russian Text]. :: Proc. Helm. Lab. Acad. Sci. USSR 16: 143-146.

1122. Szczygiel, A. 1962.
A new soil nematode Tylencholaimellus polonicus sp. n. (Nematoda, Leptonchidae) from Poland. :: Bull. Acad. Polon. Sci., Cl. II, 10(11): 473-477.

1123. Szczygiel, A. 1965.
Taxonomic status of Tarjania Brzeski & Szczygiel and redescription of Dorylaimoides bulbosus (Brzeski & Szczygiel, 1961) n. comb. (Nematoda: Leptonchidae). :: Nematologica 11(3): 409-412.

1124. Tarjan, A. C. 1960.
A review of the genus Paratylenchus Micoletzky, 1922 (Paratylenchinae: Nematoda) with a description of two new species. :: Ann. New York Acad. Sci. 84(10): 329-390.

1125. Tarjan, A. C. 1964.
A compendium of the genus Tylenchorhynchus (Tylenchidae: Nematoda). :: Proc. Helminth. Soc. Washington 31(2): 270-280.

1126. Tarjan, A. C. 1964.
Two new American dagger nematodes (Xiphinema: Dorylaimidae) associated with citrus, with comments on the variability of X. bakeri Williams, 1961. :: Proc. Helminth. Soc. Washington 31(1): 65-76.

1127. Tarjan, A. C. 1964.
Two new mucronate-tailed spiral nematodes (Helicotylenchus: Hoplolaiminae) :: Nematologica 10(2): 185-191.

1128. Tarjan, A. C. and M. Luc. 1963.
Observations on Xiphinema insigne Loos, 1949 and Xiphinema elongatum Schuurmans Stekhoven & Teunissen, 1938 (Nematoda: Dorylaimidae). :: Nematologica 9(2): 163-172.

1129. Tarjan, A. C. and B. Weischer. 1965.
Observations on some Pratylenchinae (Nemata), with additional data on *Pratylenchoides guevarai* Tobar Jiménez, 1963 (syn: *Zygotylenchus browni* Siddiqi, 1963 and *Mesotylus gallicus* de Guiran, 1964). :: Nematologica 11(3): 432-440.

1130. Taylor, D. P. 1964.
Butlerius monhystera (Nematoda, Diplogasterinae), a new species of predaceous nematode from Illinois. :: Proc. Helminth. Soc. Washington 31(2): 129-132.

1131. Thomas, P. R. and M. W. Allen. 1965.
Two new species of *Acrobeles* and a redescription of the type, *A. ciliatus* Linstow, 1877. :: Nematologica 11(3): 373-382.

1132. Thorne, G. 1961.
Principles of nematology. :: McGraw-Hill Book Co., Inc., New York, 553 pp.

1133. Thorne, G. 1964.
Nematodes of Puerto Rico: Belondiroidea new superfamily, Leptonchidae, Thorne, 1935, and Belonenchidae new family (Nemata, Adenophorea, Dorylaimida). :: Univ. Puerto Rico Agr. Exp. Sta. Tech. Paper 39, 51 pp.

1133a. Timm, R. W. 1960.
Brevibucca punctata, n. sp. and *Macrolaimus natator,* n. sp., new soil nematodes from East Pakistan. :: Biologia, Pakistan 6: 252-256.

1134. Timm, R. W. 1960.
Paraseinura (Nematoda: Aphelenchoididae), a new genus from East Pakistan. :: Nematologica 5(3): 171-174.

1135. Timm, R. W. 1960.
The widespread occurrence of the hemizonid. :: Nematologica 5(2): 150.

1136. Timm, R. W. 1961.
Five species of Diplogaster (Nematoda, Diplogasterida) from East Pakistan. :: Pakistan J. Biol. Agr. Sci. 4(1): 1-6.

1137. Timm, R. W. 1961.
Prodontorhabditis, n. gen. (Rhabditidae: Prodontorhabditinae n. subf.), a new soil nematode from East Pakistan. :: Proc. Helminth. Soc. Washington 28(2): 115-117.

1137a. Timm, R. W. 1961.
The systematic position of *Isolaimium* Cobb, 1920 (Nematoda), with a description of a new species. :: Jour. Bombay Nat. Hist. Soc. 58(1): 302-304.

1138. Timm. R. W. 1963.
A redescription of *Demaniella cibourgensis* Steiner, 1914 (Nematoda: Diplogasteridae). :: Biologia, Pakistan 9(2): 49-51.

1139. Timm, R. W. 1963.
Tylenchorhynchus trilineatus n. sp. from West Pakistan, with notes on *T. nudus* and *T. martini.* :: Nematologica 9(2): 262-266.

1140. Timm, R. W. 1964.
Nematodes of the superfamily Dorylaimoidea from East Pakistan. :: Proc. Helminth. Soc. Washington 31(2): 144-153.

1141. Timm, R. W. 1965.
Scutellonema siamense n. sp. (Tylenchida: Hoplolaiminae) from Thailand. :: Nematologica 11(3): 370-372.

1142. Timm, R. W. and M. Ameen. 1960.
Nygellus subclavatus, a new species of free-living soil nematode. :: Pakistan J. Biol. & Agr. Sci. 2(2): 1-2.

1143. Timm, R. W. and A. Q. Bhuiyan. 1963.
Discolaimium pakistanicum n. sp. (Nematoda: Dorylaimidae), with a key to the species of *Discolaimium.* :: Biologia, Pakistan 9(2): 53-56.

1144. Tobar Jiménez, A. 1963.
Pratylenchoides guevarai n. sp., nuevo nematode tylénchido, relacionado con el ciprés (*Cupressus sempervirens* L.). :: Rev. Ibérica Parasit. 23(1/2): 27-36.

1144a. Tobar Jiménez, A. [1964]. *Ditylenchus virtudesae* n. sp. (Nematoda: Tylenchidae), habitante de los suelos granadinos. :: Rev. Ibérica Parasit. 24(1/2): 51-56.

1144b. Tsalolikhin, S. T. [1965]. A new saprobiotic nematode, *Panagrellus silusioides* n. sp. [Russian Text]. :: Vest. Leningr. Gos. Univ. 20(21): 152-153.

1144c. Wallace, H. R. and D. N. Greet. 1964. Observations on the taxonomy and biology of *Tylenchorhynchus macrurus* (Goodey, 1932) Filipjev, 1936 and *Tylenchorhynchus icarus* sp. nov. :: Parasitology 54: 129-144.

1145. Waseem, M. 1961. Two new species of the genus Helicotylenchus Steiner, 1945 (Nematoda: Hoplolaiminae). :: Canad. J. Zool. 39(4): 505-509.

1145a. Wasilewska, Lucyna. [1965]. *Ditylenchus medicaginis* sp. n., a new parasitic nematode from Poland (Nematoda, Tylenchidae). :: Bull. Acad. Polon. Sci., Cl. II, 13(3): 167-170.

1145b. Wasilewska, Lucyna. [1965]. Tylenchus sandneri sp. n. a new nematode from Poland (Nematoda, Tylenchidae). :: Bull. Acad. Polon. Sci., Cl. II, 13: 87-89.

1146. Weischer, B. 1962. *Desmoscolex vinealis* n. sp. and *Pareudesmoscolex verrucosus* n. g., n. sp., die ersten bodenbewohnenden Desmoscoleciden (Nematoda: Desmoscolecidae). :: Zool. Anz., Leipzig 168(5/6): 229-235.

1147. Williams, J. R. 1960. Studies on the nematode soil fauna of sugar cane fields in Mauritius. 4. Tylenchoidea (*partim*). :: Mauritius Sugar Ind. Res. Inst., Occ. Paper 4, 30 pp., 2 pl.

1148. Williams, J. R. 1962. A new genus and species of Nygolaimidae (Enoplida). :: Nematologica 8(3): 225-228.

1149. Williams, J. R. 1964. Studies on the nematode soil fauna of sugar cane fields in Mauritius. 6. *Eudorylaimus sundarus* n. sp. (Dorylaimidae). :: Nematologica 10(2): 319-322.

1150. Williams, J. R. 1964. Studies on the nematode soil fauna of sugar cane fields in Mauritius. 7. Species of *Thornenema* (Dorylaimidae). :: Nematologica 10(3): 345-352.

1151. Williams, T. D. 1961. Xiphinema bakeri n. sp. (Nematoda: Longidorinae) from the Fraser River Valley, British Columbia, Canada. :: Canad. J. Zool. 39(4): 407-412.

1152. Wilski, A. 1964. The nematode plant-parasitic fauna of glasshouse soils in Poland [Polish Text]. :: Prace Nauk. Inst. Ochrony Roślin. 6(1): 5-59.

1153. Wu, Liang-Yu. 1960. Criconema celetum n. sp. (Nematoda: Criconematidae) from African violets in Canada. :: Canad. J. Zool. 38(5): 913-916.

1154. Wu, Liang-Yu. 1961. Paratylenchus tenuicaudatus n. sp. (Nematoda: Criconematidae). :: Canad. J. Zool. 39: 163-165.

1155. Wu, Liang-Yu. 1962. Paratylenchus brevihastus n. sp. (Criconematidae: Nematoda). :: Canad. J. Zool. 40: 391-393.

1156. Wu, Liang-Yu. 1962. Paratylenchus veruculatus n. sp. (Criconematidae: Nematoda) from Scotland. :: Canad. J. Zool. 40: 773-775.

1157. Wu, Liang-Yu. 1964. Bakernema n. gen. (Criconematidae: Nematoda). :: Canad. J. Zool. 42: 921.

1158. Wu, Liang-Yu. 1964.
Criconema bakeri n. sp. (Criconematidae: Nematoda). :: Canad. J. Zool. 42: 53-57.

1159. Wu, Liang-Yu. 1965.
Criconema seymouri n. sp. (Criconematidae: Nematoda). :: Canad. J. Zool. 43: 215-217.

1160. Wu, Liang-Yu. 1965.
Five new species of Criconemoides Taylor, 1936 (Criconematinae: Nematoda) from Canada. :: Canad. J. Zool. 43: 203-214.

1160a. Yokoo, T. 1963.
A new ring nematode, Hemicriconemoides ureshinoensis n. sp., found in the soil around the root of tea-plant with some notes on its distribution in the soil. :: Agr. Bull. Saga Univ. 16: 31-35.

1160b. Yokoo, T. 1964.
On a new species of Aphelenchoides (Aphelenchidae: Nematoda), parasite of bulb of lily, from Japan. :: Agr. Bull. Saga Univ. 20: 67-69.

1160c. Yokoo, T. [1964].
On a new species of ring nematode from Japan. II. :: Agr. Bull. Saga Univ. 20: 63-65.

1160d. Yokoo, T. 1964.
On the stubby root nematodes from the Western Japan. :: Agr. Bull. Saga Univ. 20: 57-62.

1161. Yokoo, T. and Y. Ota. 1961.
On the variations of dimensions within soil nematodes. III. Dimensions of the *Brevibucca japonica* n. sp. found in the decayed fruit of pear in Japan with descriptions of this new species. :: Agr. Bull. Saga Univ. 12: 149-156.

1162. Yuen, Pick H. 1964.
Four new species of *Helicotylenchus* Steiner (Hoplolaiminae: Tylenchida) and a redescription of *H. canadensis* Waseem, 1961. :: Nematologica 10(3): 373-387.

1163. Zopf, W. 1888.
Zur Kenntnis der Infections-Krankheiten niederer Thiere und Pflanzen. :: Nova Acta Ksl. Leop.-Carol. Deut. Akad. Naturf. 52(7): 315-376, 7 Tab.

1164. Zuckerman, B. M., J. P. Reed, and W. R. Jenkins. 1964.
Notes on *Hemicycliophora vaccinium* Reed & Jenkins. :: Nematologica 9(4) (1963): 648.